McCORMICK-MATHERS CHALLENGE READERS

AIMING HIGH

GAINING NEW HEIGHTS

REACHING AHEAD

AIMING HIGH

Lee Harrison Mountain

Reading Consultant
Hanover Park Regional
School District
Hanover, New Jersey

Walter M. Mason

Professional Writer
for Children

McCormick–Mathers Challenge Readers

McCormick–Mathers Publishing Company, Inc.
Wichita, Kansas

Grateful acknowledgment is made for the help of the following members of the Bridgewater-Raritan School District, Raritan, New Jersey:

Mrs. Ellen Middelstaedt,
Elementary Reading Supervisor

Mrs. Adelaide Kenney,
Principal of Valley School, Martinsville

Mrs. Teresa Kelly,
Principal of Raritan Elementary School

Mrs. Catherine Henry,
Teacher, Valley School, Martinsville

Mrs. Constance Tozzi,
Teacher, Raritan Elementary School

Illustrated by:
Harold Berson • Eddie Chan • Hertha Depper
W. T. Mars • Herbert McClure • Harvey Kidder
Carol Wilde

Stories

v

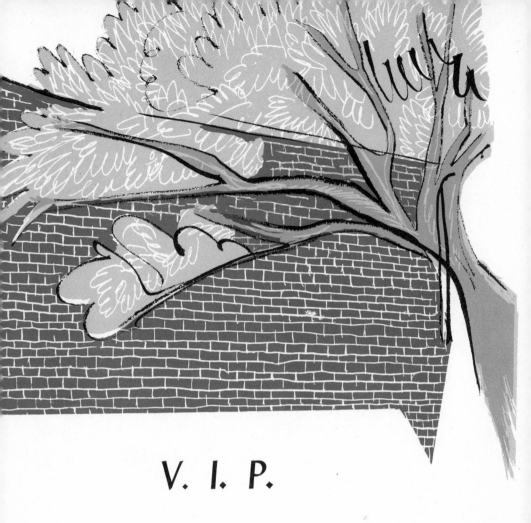

V. I. P.

Roy Parker pushed up the garage door and led Paul and Harry inside. Then he pointed to an old circus poster on one wall. "That's a picture of my Uncle Arnold," said Roy. "Now will you fellows believe that my uncle really is a juggler?"

"That's a picture of a juggler, all right," said Paul. "But how do we know that the juggler in the picture is really your uncle?"

"That's easy," said Roy. "Look at the name on the poster. It's Parker, the same as mine."

Paul read the words on the poster — *Arnold Parker, World's Greatest Juggler*. Then he said, "All right, Roy. I believe you."

"Look at those knives!" said Harry. "Six of them, and big ones, too! Does your uncle really juggle six knives, Roy?"

"Not only that," Roy answered as he pointed toward the top of the picture. "Look how he does it — blindfolded!"

"Real knives?" asked Paul.

"Real knives," said Roy.

"Sharp?" asked Harry. Then he answered himself. "No, the knives wouldn't have to be sharp. If they aren't used for anything but juggling, they needn't be a bit sharp."

"That's where you're wrong, Harry," said Roy. "Uncle Arnold sharpens those knives as part of his act. Then he tosses a piece of paper into the air and cuts it in two. That proves how sharp the knives are."

"How about the blindfold?" asked Paul. "Is it fixed so your uncle can see through it?"

"Putting on the blindfold is another important part of the act," said Roy. "Uncle Arnold always

2

asks someone to come up on the stage and try the blindfold."

"Boy!" said Harry. "Imagine juggling six big, sharp knives without being able to see them. I can't think of a better way to lose an arm."

ARNOLD PARKER

WORLDS GREATEST JUGGLER

"What do you mean by that, Harry?" asked Roy. His voice was suddenly louder.

"Well, don't get upset, Roy," said Harry. "I didn't mean anything except what I said. A man could get hurt doing an act like that."

"Why did you say my Uncle Arnold had lost an arm?" asked Roy.

"I didn't say that," answered Harry. "I just said — oh, never mind. Let's do what we came in here for. Let's see if this garage is a good place to practice our act for the school show. What do you think about it, Paul?"

Paul looked around the garage. "I like it," he said. "There's plenty of room. Besides, how can we go wrong with the greatest juggler in the world right here to watch us?"

"It's a good thing he's blindfolded," said Harry. "I think our little act would look pretty silly to the world's greatest juggler. He might feel like throwing a knife at us."

"Stop that, Harry!" said Roy, and again his voice was loud. This time his face was red, too. "You sound as if you're making fun of my Uncle Arnold. If you had an uncle who was a very important person, you wouldn't want me to make fun of him, would you?"

4

"No," said Harry, "I wouldn't want anybody to make fun of him. But I don't know why you think I'm making fun of your uncle. I've never seen you so touchy, Roy."

"Come on, fellows," said Paul. "Let's decide about this garage. Shall we meet here Saturday afternoon and practice our act?"

"That's fine with me if it's all right with Roy," said Harry. "After all, it's Roy's garage, and if he doesn't want us to use it, well . . . ."

"Certainly I want us to use this garage," said Roy. "So you two come on over here Saturday afternoon, and we'll practice."

"All right, Roy," said Harry. "We'll be here. So long."

thinking about what you have read

1. Why did Harry and Paul go into Roy's garage? Was it to see the picture of the juggler? Or was it to see whether the garage was a good place to practice an act?

2. What was the first thing Roy did when the boys went into his garage? Was it to show how much room the garage had for practicing an act? Or was it to show off the picture of his uncle?

5

3. Now think about your answer to question 2. Does it seem to show that Roy was bragging about having an uncle who was a very important person?

4. Read paragraph 1 on page 1 again. Does its last sentence tell you that Roy had been bragging about his uncle before he and his friends reached the garage?

5. Does it seem to say that Harry and Paul had not quite believed Roy's story about his Uncle Arnold?

6. Read paragraph 2 on page 1 again. Does it seem to show that Paul was still not too sure that Roy was telling the truth?

7. Reread paragraph 3 on page 2. Does it seem to show that Harry believed Roy but might not have believed the picture?

8. In paragraph 2 on page 3, Harry said, "I can't think of a better way to lose an arm." Then in paragraph 6 on page 4, Harry said, "He might feel like throwing a knife at us." Both times, Roy's voice became loud. The second time his face became red, too. Did Roy seem to be very touchy about his uncle?

9. If so, was his touchiness explained anywhere in the first part of the story?

10. In real life, have you seen people get touchy for reasons that you cannot explain?
Now let's go on with the story.

That night at dinner, Roy's father had some news for the Parker family.

"My brother Arnold called me this afternoon," said Mr. Parker. "He said he would be traveling this way on Saturday and would stop to see us."

"Oh, that's wonderful news!" said Mrs. Parker. "Just think, Roy. Since your Uncle Arnold will be here on a Saturday, you can spend the whole day with him."

Roy looked down at his plate. "Does Uncle Arnold have to come on Saturday?" he asked. "Can't he come some other day?"

"Why, Roy!" said his mother. "You sound as if you don't want to see your Uncle Arnold."

"I'd like to see him," said Roy, "but I've made plans for Saturday."

"Roy," asked Mr. Parker, "what kind of plans have you made? They must be very important to keep you from wanting to see your uncle."

"Harry and Paul are coming over here Saturday," said Roy. "We're going to practice an act in the garage."

"What kind of act, Roy?" asked his mother.

"Oh, it's just a little act for a school show," said Roy. "Harry does a magic trick, and Paul tells some jokes, and I juggle a little. That's all."

"Let me make sure I understand," said Mr. Parker. "On Saturday you plan to practice an act in which you juggle a little. And you plan to do

your practicing in our garage, where your Uncle Arnold's picture covers part of one wall. And you plan to have two of your friends in there with you. Is that right, Roy?"

"Yes, sir," said Roy.

"Roy," said Mr. Parker, "is there something about your uncle that you don't want your friends to know?"

"Well, it isn't any of their business," said Roy.

"You didn't answer my question, Roy," said Mr. Parker. "So let me ask the question in another way. Did you tell your friends that your Uncle Arnold was a juggler?"

"Yes," said Roy. "I showed them his picture."

"Now listen carefully and answer carefully, Roy," said Mr. Parker. "Did you tell your friends that your Uncle Arnold once was a juggler? Or did you tell them that he is now a juggler?"

Roy's face turned red as he looked at his plate. His voice was so low it could hardly be heard as he said, "I guess I said *is*."

"I think I understand," said Mr. Parker. "If you said *is* instead of *was*, I think you must have forgotten some other things. Did you tell your friends that your uncle lost an arm in an automobile accident?"

9

"No, sir," said Roy.

"Did you tell them that your Uncle Arnold is now a businessman?"

"No, sir."

"You aren't ashamed of your uncle because he has only one arm, are you?"

"No, sir."

"You aren't ashamed of him because he is a businessman, are you?"

"No, sir."

"All right, Roy," said Mr. Parker. "Now I understand, and I'm proud of you."

Roy, who had been staring at his plate, looked up in surprise. "You're proud of me, Dad? Why?"

"I am proud of you because I know what you are ashamed of," said Mr. Parker. "I would be sorry if you were ashamed of your Uncle Arnold because he has only one arm. I would be sorry if you were ashamed of him because he no longer gets his picture printed on posters. I'm proud of you because you are ashamed of something you did that was not right."

"I know what you mean," said Roy. "I told a whopper, and I'm ashamed of it."

"Roy," said his mother, "you have made the kind of mistake that almost everybody makes at one time or another. Many people do not know why they make that mistake. Do you know why you told what you now admit was a whopper?"

Roy thought a while before he answered. "That's funny," he said. "Maybe I should know why I told a whopper, but I don't."

"You might understand the reason better if you saw someone else make the same mistake," said Mrs. Parker. "Think about little Freddie, for example. You know the kind of whopper he tells."

"Yes, I know Freddie," said Roy. "His father works in a bank. I don't know what his job is, but Freddie tells everybody that his father has shot hundreds of bank robbers."

"Telling that whopper is Freddie's way of bragging about what a very important person his father is," said Mrs. Parker. "Saying that his father has shot hundreds of bank robbers does not seem like a lie to Freddie. He doesn't know any facts that would prove how important his father is, so he makes up the story about robbers. It is the only way he can think of to prove what he thinks is the truth — that his father is important."

"Doesn't Freddie know that nobody believes him?" asked Roy.

"As a matter of fact," said Mrs. Parker, "I believe Freddie. Oh, I don't believe what he says about the robbers. But I believe what Freddie means. He means that his father is a very important person."

"That's the way we believe you, too, Roy," said Mr. Parker. "We believe what you meant, not what you said, about your Uncle Arnold."

"Anyway," said Roy, "my whopper wasn't as big as little Freddie's."

"I wouldn't be too sure about that," said Mrs. Parker. "Nobody believes little Freddie's whopper, but Paul and Harry must believe that your uncle is still a juggler."

"I have to tell Paul and Harry the truth, don't I?" said Roy.

"Roy, are you going to feel embarrassed about that?" asked his father.

"Yes," said Roy. "I'm sure I am."

"I think that somebody is likely to be embarrassed on Saturday," said Mr. Parker. "Harry and Paul should know the truth before they meet your uncle. Otherwise they may say something that will embarrass him or themselves. If somebody has to be embarrassed, I think it should be the one who most deserves it. That certainly isn't your uncle, and I don't think it is either Paul or Harry."

"That leaves me," said Roy. "I'm the one who told the whopper, so I'm the one who deserves to be embarrassed."

thinking about what you have read

1. On page 3 you were told that Harry looked at the picture of a blindfolded man who was juggling six knives. Then Harry jokingly said, "I can't think of a better way to lose an arm." You now know some facts that you did not know when you first read that remark.

   a. At the time Harry made that remark, did Roy's uncle still have both arms?

b.   Did he still make his living as a juggler?

c.   Although you know the answers to questions 1a and 1b, did Harry know them?

d.   Whose fault was it that Harry did not know the truth about Roy's uncle?

e.   You will remember that Roy seemed to be upset by Harry's remark. Was it really Harry's remark that upset Roy, or was it instead Roy's own whopper that upset him?

2.   Roy was also upset in the first scene because Harry said, "He might feel like throwing a knife at us." Harry of course said that as a joke. But Roy thought Harry was making fun of his Uncle Arnold. There is a difference between making a joke about somebody and making fun of somebody. To make fun of a person is like trying to make that person seem unimportant.

a.   Was Harry's joke meant to make Roy's uncle seem unimportant?

b.   Was Harry's joke just his way of saying, "Our act is not good enough to put on in front of a great juggler like your uncle"?

c.   Would Roy have been upset by Harry's joke if he had told the truth about his uncle?

3.   The story about little Freddie helped Roy to understand why he had told his whopper.

a.   What was true about Freddie's whopper — that his father was important or that his father had shot hundreds of bank robbers?

b. What was true about Roy's whopper — that his uncle was a very important person or that he was still the world's greatest juggler?

c. Were both boys making up untrue stories to try to prove what they really believed to be true?

4. In the first scene of this story, in the garage, Roy did something wrong. In the second scene of this story, at home, Roy did something right by admitting what he had done. But Roy has not yet made up for what he did wrong. In order to make up for it, must he let his friends know the truth?

On Saturday afternoon, Harry and Paul came to Roy's house. Roy took them out to the garage and opened the door.

"Look!" said Paul. "Somebody has covered up the picture of the juggler."

Sure enough, a big piece of paper had been pinned over the picture of Roy's Uncle Arnold. Not only that, but a small picture had been pinned to the piece of paper.

Paul and Harry stepped up to take a close look at the small picture. "Why, it's a picture of Roy," said Paul.

"Look at that!" said Harry. "Roy has put his picture over the words, *World's Greatest Jug-*

16

gler. Now if that isn't a whopper, I don't know what one is!"

"Just a minute, fellows," said Roy. "I haven't finished changing the poster."

Roy took another piece of paper and put it over the word *Juggler.* Then on that piece of paper he wrote *Whopper-Teller.*

"I guess it's a joke of some kind, but I don't get the point," said Paul.

"I think I get it," said Harry. "Roy must have told a whopper when he said that the picture of the juggler was a picture of his uncle. Maybe that is why he was so touchy the other day when he thought I was making fun of his uncle. I'm beginning to wonder if he even has an uncle."

A man's laugh sounded behind the boys, and they turned to see a one-armed man standing in the doorway. "Roy has an uncle, all right," said the man. "I am his Uncle Arnold. I used to be a juggler."

"Used to be?" said Paul. "I thought that Roy said . . . ."

"I don't know what Roy said because I didn't hear him," said Uncle Arnold. "But I know what Roy felt. I know how Roy feels about jugglers because I felt the same way at his age. I thought

17

that being a juggler was the most important thing in the world. That is why I wanted to be the greatest juggler in the world — until an automobile accident changed my mind."

"You were the greatest juggler, too, Uncle Arnold," said Roy.

"Maybe," said Uncle Arnold. "Maybe not. The thing to remember now is that Roy thought I was a great juggler. So to him I am a V.I.P. Do you know what a V.I.P is, boys?"

"I do," said Paul. "The letters V.I.P. stand for Very Important Person."

"Right," said Uncle Arnold. "Now remember that Roy thought of me as a V.I.P., and he also thought of me as his uncle. Would you expect him to say anything about me that would make me seem unimportant?"

18

"No," said Harry. "He wouldn't even let any-body else say anything that made you seem unimportant. He was mighty touchy when he thought I was making fun of you."

"Good for him," said Uncle Arnold. "I'd be touchy, too, if somebody made fun of Roy. I can understand how Roy couldn't think of me as a has-been juggler. That would be like saying that I used to be a V.I.P. but no longer am. So Roy said *is* when he should have said *was*. Isn't that right, Roy?"

"Yes, it is," said Roy.

Uncle Arnold pointed to Roy's picture on the wall. "Roy," he asked, "do you now claim to be the world's greatest whopper-teller just because you said *is* instead of *was*?"

"Yes, I guess so," said Roy.

"Let's see how much of a whopper-teller you are," said Uncle Arnold. "How many balls do you use in your juggling act?"

"Three," said Roy.

"Only three!" shouted Uncle Arnold. "You use only three balls with two hands! And you call that juggling? Why, you are a whopper-teller, Roy. Toss me those three balls, and we'll see what a has-been juggler can do with them."

There in the garage the man who had once been called the world's greatest juggler put on a show. He juggled those three balls so fast that

they looked like six. He bounced them on the floor. He bounced them against the wall. He juggled them with his shoulders. He juggled them with his knees. And all the while one sleeve of his coat hung quietly empty at his side.

When the show was over, Harry said, "I never saw anything like it, Mr. Parker. You must really be the world's greatest juggler."

"No," said Uncle Arnold. "I'm just the best juggler you've seen today in this garage. I hope I've proved more than that a has-been juggler can still juggle. I hope I've proved that Roy was not as big a whopper-teller as he thinks he was. As long as Roy thinks of himself as a whopper-teller, he can't think of himself as the V.I.P. I know he is."

thinking about what you have read

1. Let's think about the way Roy let his friends know the truth.

   a. What was the truth that Roy had to let Paul and Harry know? Was it that his uncle was no longer a juggler, or was it that his uncle had never been a juggler?

   b. Did Roy tell the truth to his friends or did he plan a way to let them find it out?

2. Let's see how well Roy's friends caught on to what he was doing.

a. Reread the last paragraph on page 16. Did Harry mistakenly think that Roy was claiming to be the world's greatest juggler?

b. Reread paragraph 5 on page 17. Did Harry mistakenly think that Roy had lied about having an uncle who had been a juggler?

c. Would Harry and Paul have learned the truth more quickly if Roy had just told them the truth?

d. By trying to show the truth instead of telling it, Roy was trying to avoid an unpleasant moment. If his friends had not caught on, do you think Roy would have told them the truth, no matter how unpleasant it was?

3. Let's see how Uncle Arnold tried to help.

a. Reread paragraph 6 on page 17. In that paragraph did Uncle Arnold tell the truth about himself?

b. Now turn back to page 1 and reread the first paragraph of the story. In that paragraph Roy could have told the truth by changing only one word in the last line. What was that word and what should it have been changed to?

c. Reread paragraph 2 on page 18. Then reread paragraph 1 on page 13. Did Uncle Arnold think of Roy's whopper just as Mrs. Parker had thought of little Freddie's whopper?

d. Did Uncle Arnold think of Roy's whopper as the kind that should be quickly forgiven or not forgiven?

e. In paragraph 2 on page 19, Uncle Arnold seemed to be praising Roy for being touchy. Usually people are not praised for that. Was Roy really being praised for being touchy, or was he being praised for loyally sticking up for his uncle?

f. When a person gets himself into an unpleasant situation, sometimes a friend can help him out of it. One good way is to draw attention away from whatever it is that makes the situation unpleasant. Did Uncle Arnold's juggling act draw attention away from the unpleasant fact that Roy had not told the truth?

Out From Under the

Julie Cranford awoke and sniffed. The smell of boiling coffee was plain enough, but what was that other smell, that new smell?

Julie crawled part way out of her sleeping bag, sat up, bumped her head against the tent, and remembered. Oh, yes. That other smell had been

Willow

with her all yesterday afternoon. It was the smell of pine trees.

Yesterday afternoon the Cranfords had driven through miles of pine trees. Then Sam, the guide who was to take them into fishing country, met them.

With Sam they had gone deep into a forest of pines until they came to a stream. Then Sam led them along the stream, crossing it now and then on rocks or logs, until they came to a quiet pool.

The Cranfords had never put up tents before. Sam told them how. Then, when knots in the tent ropes came loose, he tightened them. When the tents looked as if they would fall, he straightened them up — and they stayed up.

Julie's father had said he knew how to build a fire. But the fire he built smoked so much that everybody's eyes watered. Then Sam poked a stick here, poked another stick there, and suddenly there was no smoke at all.

"You certainly know your business, Sam," Mr. Cranford said.

"You are a wonder, Sam," Mrs. Cranford added.

But Julie, who thought that Sam had made her mother and father look foolish, said nothing.

Now, as she lay in her tent, Julie was glad she had said nothing to Sam. She would keep on saying nothing to him. She wouldn't give him a chance to make her look foolish. She —

"Miss Julie, what would you like to drink this morning — hot milk or chocolate?" It was Sam's voice, right beside her tent.

26

In the first scene of this story, you found Julie Cranford lying in a sleeping bag inside a tent. You knew where she was before you had finished reading the second paragraph. When you had finished reading the last paragraph on page 26, you knew that she was still there.

Between paragraph 2 on page 24 and the last paragraph on page 26, you followed Julie's thinking. Her thinking led you back over what had happened since she had met Sam.

1. Let's see what you have learned about the Cranford family.

a. Did paragraph 2 on page 26, about putting up the tents, make you think that the Cranfords were expert campers?

b. Did paragraph 3 on page 26, about building a fire, help you to make up your mind about the Cranfords as campers?

c. In paragraphs 4 and 5 on page 26, Mr. and Mrs. Cranford both praised Sam for doing what they could not do. Did these paragraphs lead you to think that they were glad to have the help of an expert?

d. In paragraph 6 on page 26, Julie did not praise Sam because she felt that he had made the Cranfords look foolish. If her mother and father had thought so, would they have praised Sam?

27

2. Let's see what you have learned about Sam.

a. Sam's job was named in paragraph 2 on page 25. What was it?

b. Is a man with such a job expected to be an expert camper?

c. Julie did not want to give Sam a chance to make her look foolish. Had Sam tried to make her, or any of the other Cranfords, look foolish?

3. Let's see what you have learned about Julie.

a. When Julie first sat up, she bumped her head against the tent. She had to think twice before she remembered the smell of pine trees. When you knew only that much about Julie, did you know that she was not an expert camper?

b. When Julie decided to have as little to do with Sam as she could, did she decide to be friendly or unfriendly?

When Julie did not answer, Sam shook her tent. "Wake up, Miss Julie. The sun's up and the trout are jumping."

Julie almost said, "Go away. I don't want to go fishing." But she was sure her mother would be listening, so she said, "Thank you, Sam. I'll get right up."

When she came out of her tent, Julie found her mother talking to Sam. "I didn't know you were going to get breakfast," Mrs. Cranford was saying. "I thought we decided to catch some trout first and cook them for breakfast."

"Oh, I wouldn't call this a breakfast," said Sam. "But we don't always catch a trout as soon as we'd like. Something warm inside makes the waiting easier."

Sam turned to Julie. "I made hot milk, but I can change it to chocolate if you like."

Julie did not like the idea of eating anything that Sam had cooked. "No, thank you," she said. "I don't —"

"I'm sure you will like the hot chocolate, Julie," said her mother. "Thank you, Sam, for making it for her."

Sam poured chocolate into the hot milk and handed it to Julie. "All three fly rods are ready," he said. "I've put on light tackle because I thought you'd want to catch small trout this morning."

"Small trout?" Mrs. Cranford seemed surprised. "I thought people always tried to catch the largest fish in the stream."

"You'll get a chance to catch some big ones," said Sam. "There should be some right here in this pool. I saw a big one a few minutes ago. He came up over there under that willow tree on the other side. But let's go downstream and catch some smaller trout. They are easier to catch and easier to cook, and I don't think you want to wait too long for your breakfast."

Mr. Cranford had picked up one of the rods and was looking at the fly at the end of its line.

"I think I'll try a cast or two right here," he said. "Maybe I can get the big one you saw under that willow."

Mr. Cranford raised the rod and swung it far back over his head. As he threw it forward, his reel buzzed. "What did I catch?" he asked in surprise.

"You caught a branch on the tree right behind you," said Sam. "Let me get the hook loose for you."

"Never mind, Sam," said Mr. Cranford. "I

can pull it loose." He pulled gently on the line, but nothing happened. He pulled a little harder, and a few leaves came floating down. Then he pulled again, and the line snapped.

"Why, it broke!" said Mr. Cranford.

"So it did," said Sam, who had already pulled off his hat and was taking a fly from it. "Some fishermen have to lose a fish or two before they find out how easy it is to break light tackle. You're learning fast, Mr. Cranford. You've lost your first hook without even getting your line wet."

"Couldn't the tackle be made stronger?" asked Mrs. Cranford.

"Yes, of course," said Sam. "If trout fishing were a business instead of a sport, we'd use much stronger tackle. Since it is a sport, we give the fish a sporting chance to get away. Using very light tackle gives the best chance to the best fish."

"Is there a way to get the hook loose from a tree without breaking the line?" asked Mr. Cranford.

"It's better not to get the hook caught in the first place," said Sam. "I'd like to see you learn to cast where there aren't any trees. Let's save this pool, which is hard to fish, until after you've tried some easier places."

"I'd like to see how good we'll have to be when we are ready to fish this pool," said Mr. Cranford. "Will you show us, Sam?"

"All right," said Sam. "Let's suppose I want to put a fly over there where I saw that big trout rise this morning."

"I know," said Mr. Cranford. "Right under the lowest branch of that willow. That's the spot I was aiming at when I hit the tree behind me."

"Suppose," said Sam, "that you wanted to stand on the other side of the pool, right where that willow is. How would you get over there, Mr. Cranford?"

"I'd go downstream to the place where we crossed yesterday," said Mr. Cranford. "Then I'd walk back up on the other side."

"Good for you," said Sam. "You'd go all that roundabout way to keep from wading straight across the pool. You need to do the same kind of thinking when you cast a fly. If you try to cast straight at that spot under the willow, your hook will catch on a branch and never reach the water. So let's find a roundabout way to get this fly where we want it without hitting a tree."

Sam gently cast upstream and let the fly float back toward him on the current.

"That's not far enough, is it?" asked Mr. Cranford.

"No," said Sam. "I didn't expect it to be. I'll have to work the fly out toward the current that will carry it under the willow."

As he s p o k e, Sam raised the tip of his rod until the line was more than half out of the water. Then, flicking the tip sharply forward, he cast the fly a few feet farther. "One more cast and I'll have that fly out there where I want it," he said. "There, now do you see how the current will carry the fly under the willow?"

"Yes," said Mr. Cranford. "Is a trout going to take it?"

"No," said Sam, swiftly pulling the fly away from the willow. "That trout belongs to somebody in the Cranford family. I don't want to catch him, and I don't want to hurt him so that you can't catch him later. Now, if you're ready, let's go downstream and see about getting a few little ones for breakfast."

"I'm ready," said Mrs. Cranford. "Come on, Julie."

"I don't want to go," said Julie.

"Why not?" asked her father.

"I wouldn't eat a trout if I caught one," said Julie. "I wouldn't even touch one. So I don't want to catch one."

"Julie, don't you feel well?" asked her mother.

"Yes, I feel all right," said Julie. "I never wanted to catch a fish before, so I don't see anything wrong with not wanting to catch one now."

"Julie," said Mr. Cranford, "all the while we were planning this trip, I thought you would be the one who would enjoy it most. What's the matter, Julie?"

"Nothing's the matter," said Julie. Then she added, "I just don't see how you can have fun when everything you do is wrong. I don't think it is any fun if somebody has to tell you what you have to do all the time."

Mrs. Cranford put her hand under Julie's chin. "I think I understand what's wrong," she said. "I'm sure you'll feel better after one of us has caught a fish. So come along with us, and maybe you'll catch the first one."

"No," said Julie, and while she was saying it she knew she would have to have a reason. Then a reason came to her so suddenly that she smiled happily. "Let me stay here and take care of the fire. Then it will be ready to cook the fish you catch."

"Well, now," said her mother, "that sounds more like the Julie I have always known. Sam, will Julie be safe here by herself?"

"Yes, Mrs. Cranford," said Sam. "We won't be very far away. We'll hear Miss Julie if she calls."

"All right, Julie," said Mrs. Cranford. "If I catch the first fish, I'll bring it right back. So have the fire ready."

thinking about what you have read

Several things happened in the second scene of this story. Let's see which, if any, of them were surprises.

1. When Mr. Cranford tried to cast a fly, he caught his hook on a tree. Then he broke his line while

trying to pull the hook loose. If you were not surprised at that, was it because he had also been unable to put up a tent or build a good fire?

2. When Sam cast his fly, he easily put it where he wanted it to go. The day before he had easily put up a tent and had easily stopped a fire from smoking. You were probably not surprised by any of this. Was that because you thought of Sam as being much smarter than Mr. Cranford? Or was it because you thought of Sam as being much more expert in camping and fishing?

3. As you know, Sam pulled his fly away from the spot where he expected a trout to take it. As you also know, he probably could have caught that trout if he had wanted to show off. Who do you think was more surprised that he did not want to show off, Julie or her father?

4. So far in this story, Julie has been described as smiling happily only once. That was when she got the idea of staying to take care of the fire while the others went fishing. If that had been an unselfish idea, it might have surprised you because Julie has not yet had a happy, unselfish thought. If you were not surprised, it was because you knew her real reason. Did she really want to be helpful, or did she want to do anything that would keep her away from Sam?

When Mr. and Mrs. Cranford had followed Sam downstream, Julie turned to the fire. She had promised to take care of it, but now she wondered whether she knew how.

She looked at the neat pile of gently burning sticks. The ones that were burning best seemed to be holding those that were just starting to burn. Julie walked around the fire, looking for sticks that might be moved to a better place. She could not find one. That Sam certainly knew his business.

Julie turned toward the pool. At the upper end, where the stream was narrow, the current was quietly swift. Only a few feet farther on, where the water deepened and darkened, Julie could see movement only in bits of foam on the top. Her eyes followed one bit of foam as it circled, almost stopped, then drifted slowly under the willow on the other side.

Julie looked back and watched other bits of foam gather slowly, twist, turn, and follow the same path. All of them disappeared under a long, slender branch of the willow. It was right there, she remembered, that Sam had pulled up his fly. Back under there, somewhere, was a trout that belonged to somebody in the Cranford family. That's what Sam had said, anyway.

Julie picked up the rod that Sam had left near the fire. She had never touched a trout rod be-

fore, and she was surprised to feel how light it was. She held it out, as she had seen Sam do, and found that it was easy to swing. She shook it gently and felt how wonderfully springy it was. It seemed almost alive.

She pulled slowly on the line and heard the reel turn — click, click, clickety-click. She pulled faster, and the clicks changed into a buzz.

She touched the point of the hook and caught her breath as she felt its hard sharpness. Then she touched the feathery softness that hid most of the hook.

Looking closely, she could see how it was made. Green and red thread had been tightly wrapped around the hook to make the body

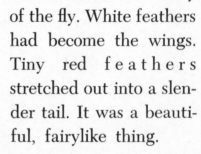

of the fly. White feathers had become the wings. Tiny red feathers stretched out into a slender tail. It was a beautiful, fairylike thing.

Letting go of the fly, she swung it out over the pool. Then she let it drop onto the water and watched it float. How wonderfully light it was, as light as the bits of foam that were drifting under the willow on the other side.

Could she make the fly drift under the willow, as Sam had done? She tried to remember just how he had done it. Really, as she thought about it, it seemed very easy. If she were careful not to get the hook caught on the tree behind her, she was sure she could make the cast.

Let's see, now. Where had Sam stood when he had made his first cast? Oh, yes. There were his footprints in the soft bank. One at a time, she placed her feet where Sam had stood.

Good. Now could she toss the fly out there where Sam had put it? Well, she could try. Stretching until she almost fell forward into the stream, Julie made her cast. It was not bad. Not far enough, but pretty good.

Now what was it that Sam had done next? Oh, yes. He had raised the tip of his rod and flicked it. That, Julie remembered, lifted the fly and threw it farther out. Julie raised the tip of her rod, flicked it, and looked for her fly on the water. She couldn't see it.

Slowly raising the rod, she tightened the line and followed it with her eyes. No wonder she hadn't seen the fly! It was caught on a high branch of the willow on the other side of the pool.

She remembered how easily her father's line had broken, and she pulled gently. The hook seemed to slip a little, and a few leaves drifted down into the water. Pulling gently again, Julie shook the branch. More leaves came twisting down to the water and floated away.

Suddenly the hook came loose, and Julie saw it drop. Then, as she pulled it quickly toward her, she felt the line tighten again. She looked

and saw that the hook had pulled loose from the
upper branch and had fallen into the water. But
her line was wrapped around the tip of the long,
slender lowest branch, about a foot above the
water. Five or six feet of line and the fly floated
lightly in the shadows.

Julie pulled gently. Nothing happened. She
pulled harder. Nothing happened. She shook the
branch. Nothing happened, except that the fly,
which had been lying quietly on top of the water,
twitched a little.

Like a flash, something seemed to explode
from the water and smash into the twitching fly.

41

At first there was too much splashing for Julie to see what was happening. Then she caught a glistening flash of the trout as it jumped clear of the water. It seemed to hang in the air for a second, shaking off water like a wet dog. Then it splashed back into the pool and disappeared.

Across the pool, the long, slender branch of the willow seemed to come alive. It shivered, bent, dipped, swung upstream and then down. Julie pulled on her rod, tightening the line between her and the tree.

"Easy, Miss Julie. I wouldn't pull yet." It was Sam's voice, right beside her. Had he come to take the rod away from her? Had he come to catch her fish, the way he had put up her father's tent and built her father's fire? If he reached for her rod, she'd —

Julie looked at Sam to see whether he was reaching for her rod. He was just standing there, staring at the bending, shivering branch of the willow. He had both hands in his pockets.

"I got your message," Sam said, "and I came as fast as I could."

Julie said nothing. She had sent no message to Sam or to anyone else.

"It was a pretty clear message," Sam went on. "Three or four little bunches of leaves floating downstream — that means a fisherman is up-stream trying to shake a hook loose from a branch. Then all that splashing — that can mean that a fisherman has got hold of a mighty fine trout. Or it can mean that a fisherman has fallen into the pool. Either way, I thought I'd better come and see if you needed any help. Looks as if you're doing just fine, all by yourself."

Julie did not think she was doing just fine. True, she was at one end of a line and a trout was at the other end. But in between there was that swaying branch of the willow tree. If any fishing was being done, the willow was doing it. Julie felt helpless.

"I don't know what to do, Sam," she said. Then, almost crying, she asked, "Is it going to get away?"

43

Sam shook his head. "I think that fish had his best chance to get away right at the start, Miss Julie. Now he's hooked and he's wearing himself out by swimming around in circles. If you just keep on doing what you are doing, I think you've got a good chance to land him."

"But I'm not doing anything," said Julie.

Sam sat down on the bank. "Mighty few fishermen are smart enough not to do anything at a time like this," he said. "You might as well sit down now. You still have quite a bit of waiting to do."

Without taking her eyes off the swaying willow branch, Julie sat down.

"You really don't need to grip that rod so hard," said Sam. "The idea is to let the fish wear himself out. You don't need to wear yourself out too, Miss Julie."

Julie nodded and loosened her grip. Then she laughed. "I didn't know I was holding it so tight until you told me."

"You're doing just right," said Sam. "By this time most fishermen would have tried to pull that willow out by its roots. All they'd have now is a broken line. But you've been smart. You've been letting the fish fight the willow and the

44

willow fight the fish. Pretty soon that fish is going to be all tired out, but you and the willow are going to be just as strong as ever. I'm counting on you to win, Miss Julie."

Suddenly Julie no longer felt helpless. Suddenly she knew that Sam would let her catch that fish, all by herself. Somehow, although she did not know how, she was sure she would catch it.

Round and round, under the branch of the willow tree, went Julie's line. As she watched the tight line cut slower and slower circles in the still water, she remembered something. A long time ago — it seemed like a very long time ago — she had not liked Sam. She tried hard to remember why, but she couldn't think of a single reason.

thinking about what you have read

Up to this point, you have been reading two stories in one. One story is about the problem of Julie's dislike for Sam. The other story is about her problem of catching a trout.

1. One of these problems seems to be almost solved.

   a. Which problem is it?

b. When did Julie first begin to lose her dislike for Sam? Was it when he first tried to be friendly to her or when she first began to trust him?

c. Why hadn't she trusted him before? Was it because he knew so much more than she did that he made her feel unimportant?

d. Before this problem can be completely solved, Julie must do something she has not yet done. Must she let Sam and her mother and father know that she no longer dislikes Sam?

2. Julie's second problem is to catch that trout.

a. So far, has she been very skillful or very lucky?

b. So far, has she thought of a way to get her line loose from that branch?

c. If she doesn't get her line loose, does she have much chance of catching that fish?

d. Do you think that Sam is going to catch that fish for Julie? Or is he going to help her find a way to catch it all by herself?

"What's going on here?" It was her father's voice. Julie turned to see him and her mother.

"I've got a fish," she said.

"I was hoping you'd come," said Sam. "Miss Julie has hooked a big one. She wants to catch it, and I think she can. But first she's got to get her

line off that branch and she can't do that without getting wet. Will you let her wade in?"

"Oh, I don't think she'll have to do that," said
Mr. Cranford. "I can go downstream, cross over
on some rocks, and walk back up the other side.
Then I can cut that branch loose."

Sam shook his head. "Wait until you see this
fish, Mr. Cranford. Then I think you'll change
your mind. This is the kind of fish that Miss Julie
will remember all her life. It's the kind she'll want
to remember catching all by herself. She's the one
who put that line around the branch, so I think
she's the one who has to take it off."

"Julie can't swim very well," said Mrs. Cranford. "How deep is the water?"

"I think it's about up to her neck, but I can't
be sure," said Sam. "She'll be in no danger because I'll wade out there with her — all the way."

"How cold?" asked Mrs. Cranford.

"Cold," said Sam. "Very close to ice cold."
Then he suddenly pointed. "Look there!"

The trout had come to the top of the water. It
was still swimming, but weakly, and part of the
time on its side. "I've seen bigger trout," said
Sam, "but not in this stream. He's a good five
pounds, and he's all yours, Miss Julie, if you
want him."

Julie started to untie her shoes. "I want him," she said. Then she turned to her mother. "I want him very much."

"All right, Julie," said Mrs. Cranford. "Go after him, and I'll find something warm to wrap you in when you come out."

"Wait one minute," said Mr. Cranford. "Give me time to get the movie camera."

"Easy now," said Sam as he stepped into the water. "This fish has plenty of life left in him. I think he'll prove that when you take the line off the willow. What are you going to do if he puts up a fight, Miss Julie?"

Julie put one foot into the water, gasped, and pulled it out again. Then she shook her head, grinned, and stepped in to her knees. "Let me — get my — breath," she gasped. "Then I'll — tell you — what I — think."

When she was halfway to the willow, the water was up to her waist. When she touched the branch that held her line, the water was up to her neck.

"Now I'll tell you what I want to do," she said. "I want to make that fish think I'm just another willow tree, so I'm going to stand still and let the fish do the pulling. Is that what you think I should do, Sam?"

"You've got the right idea," said Sam. "Now keep the rod high with your right hand. Keep it high while you work the line loose with your left hand. Try to get the line loose without letting the fish feel any change in the pull."

Julie nodded, raised her rod, and reached for the loop around the branch. Slowly, as if she were stretching a rubber band, she loosened the loop. Then she slipped it off over the end of the branch.

Now for the first time she felt the heaviness of the fish. Then, suddenly, the trout started a rush downstream.

Julie, up to her neck in icy water, was already almost floating. She had no foothold. She could not pull back. She could not stand up. She could only hang on or let go. She held on and was pulled along.

She was off her feet for only a second when the fish turned and headed back upstream. Stumbling and splashing, she heard Sam call to her. "Keep the rod high. High, Julie, high! Keep the rod high and the line tight!"

Julie found her footing in waist-deep water and stopped splashing. She shook her head to get the water out of her eyes. Then she looked up to make sure that her rod was high. It was.

She followed the line down to the water. There, quietly floating on its side, was her trout.

"Shorten the line a little," said Sam. "Use the reel."

Julie turned the reel. Now the trout was where she could reach out and touch it.

"Now what?" she asked.

"Now you do what a willow tree can't do," said Sam. "Now you slip two fingers up through the gills and lift your fish out of the water."

Julie looked down at the gasping fish, wondering what and where its gills were.

"Just grab him where he's gasping," said Sam. Julie grabbed.

Later, as she sat wrapped in blankets by the fire, Julie's father took the film out of his camera. "When we got here," he said, "I wanted to stay two weeks. Now I feel like going right back to the city to get this film developed."

Julie shook her head. "When I got here," she said, "I wanted to go right back home. Now I want to stay here until Sam can teach me how to catch fish without getting wet."

thinking about what you have read

In the last scene of this story, Julie's father took pictures with a movie camera. Let's think about what the movie would show and what it could not show.

1. The movie would show Julie as she stepped into the water. It might also show her gasp as she suddenly

felt its icy coldness. But you know something that the movie could not show. Was the Julie at the end of the story different from the Julie you knew at the beginning?

2. The movie would certainly show Julie catching the trout. It certainly would not show Sam so much as touching the rod, the line, or the trout. But you know something the movie could not show.

   a. Could Julie have caught that trout if Sam had not helped her by telling her what to do?

   b. Could Julie have caught the trout if Sam had not helped her by making her think that she could catch it?

The Winning W's

For as long as he could remember, Don Bradley had been making the same trip every year. Every year, on August 15, the Bradleys went to the County Fair.

For Mr. and Mrs. Bradley, August 15 was partly a day away from summer work on the Bradley farm. It was partly a day of visiting with relatives from all over the county. It was partly a day of looking at prize calves, prize ears of corn, prize heads of lettuce, prize jars of jelly, prize apple pies — at just about any kind of prize you could think of.

For Don Bradley, August 15 was not partly this and partly that. August 15 was a day to look forward to and a day to remember as his special day of the year. August 15 was Don's birthday.

Ever since Don could remember, his birthday present had been a trip to the County Fair. And his father had always said, "You can buy anything you want at the fair, Don, just so you-know-what."

Don knew what, all right. He knew he could buy anything he wished, anything at all, just so he didn't spend more than a dollar.

Mrs. Bradley always worried about that. "It's dangerous to turn a boy loose at the fair with a whole dollar. He might buy himself enough candy and soda to make himself sick."

She needn't have worried. Don had never used

any part of his dollar to buy candy and soda.
Why should he? After all, he knew what was in
the family picnic basket.

That basket was loaded with ham sandwiches,
beef sandwiches, cheese sandwiches, fried chick-
en, baked beans, potato salad, sweet pickles, sour
pickles, dill pickles, apple pie, lemon pie, chocolate cake, white cake, and lemonade. Mrs. Bradley
always put up enough lunch for ten people "just
in case we meet some people who might not
bring enough."

The Bradleys had never met those people
"who might not bring enough." All of the Bradleys' friends and relatives brought enough lunch
for themselves and two or three other families.

Once all that lunch was opened and piled high
on a long picnic table, not even the Bradleys and

their neighbors and relatives could eat it all. But they tried. They always tried, and no one ever tried harder than Don Bradley.

So it had always been on August 15. So it was this year, this very special August 15, on which Don Bradley became twelve years old.

Ever since Don could remember, the highlight of the fair had been the foot races. They always started at two o'clock. There were men's races, women's races, girls' races, and boys' races.

The most important race, Don thought, was the race for boys over twelve and under fourteen. The prize for that race was always a little silver statue of a barefoot runner with wings on his heels.

All year, Don had been looking forward to August 15 with just one thought in mind. He would win that prize, right in front of all his relatives and neighbors. Then he would bring it to the picnic table and set it up on top of the tallest basket there. That would be his birthday surprise to everybody he knew.

Today the birthday dollar was still in Don's pocket when lunch time came. He had been too excited to spend it. He had been too excited to think of anything he wanted to buy. As a matter of fact, there wasn't anything he wanted to buy. The only thing he wanted didn't have to be bought. The barefoot silver statue only needed to be won.

Don had just finished his fried chicken and his fourth sandwich when somebody said, "Why, Don, every sandwich on your plate is made with white bread. Here, try these whole-wheat sandwiches."

Don really wasn't very hungry, but he thought he should eat what was on his plate. By the time he had eaten the sandwiches on his plate — and two kinds of salads — and three kinds of pickles, he hoped nobody would offer him pie. He should have known better.

"I don't suppose you want much more to eat," said his mother. "So here's a small piece of apple pie and a small piece of lemon pie. You can choose between chocolate cake and white cake if you don't want both."

"Don't starve the boy," said Don's Aunt Bertha. "Here, Don, try this banana cream pie. I just don't know why my Herman won't eat any of it today."

Across the table, Don's cousin Herman sat with
an empty plate in front of him. "Aren't you eating
anything, Herman?" asked Don.

"Not until after the race," said Herman.

"Are you twelve?" asked Don.

"I'm twelve and a half," said Herman. "Why
aren't you in the race?"

Don waited a moment before he answered. He
had never told anyone that he wanted to enter

that race. He had wanted to surprise everybody by winning it. "What makes you think I'm not in the race?" he asked.

Herman laughed and pointed at Don's plate. "Sprinters eat after a race, not before," he said.

Don shook his head. "Big shot sprinters, maybe, but this race is just for kids."

"But you'd like to win, wouldn't you?" asked Herman.

To answer yes or no, Don would have to make his secret wish known. He would have to spoil the surprise that he had been saving for as long as he could remember. He looked down at his plate, finished the last bite of banana cream pie, and drank the last of his lemonade. "What time is it?" he asked his mother.

"It's ten minutes to two," she said. "My, if we don't get over to the track, we'll miss seeing the first race. Why don't you and Herman go on ahead so you'll be sure to see that race for boys of your own age? You do want to see that one, don't you?"

Don could hardly say that he wanted to see the race he expected to win. And he couldn't spoil the surprise by telling his mother that he expected to win it. So he just nodded.

"Come on, Don," said Herman. "Let's get over to the track."

Don turned back to his mother. "You and Dad will get there in time for the boys' race, won't you? It's going to be pretty special this year."

"Of course, Don," said his mother. "We'll be there, and we'll look for you somewhere in the crowd. Good-by, now."

"Good-by," said Don. He wanted to say, "Don't look for me in the crowd. Look for me on the track, out in front." But he didn't say it. That would spoil the surprise.

"Come on," said Herman. "Let's jog over to the track. A little warm-up will do us good."

Don nodded and jogged a few steps. Then he slowed to a walk. "I wish you had eaten your own banana cream pie," he said to Herman.

thinking about what you have read

1. So far in this story you have met Don Bradley, his mother, his father, his Aunt Bertha, and his cousin Herman.

   a. Which of these characters is the hero of this story?

b. In real life, a hero is someone of unusual courage, unusual strength, or unusual goodness. Does this story have that kind of hero, or is its hero the character who gets most of a reader's attention?

2. So far in this story you have been reading about a county fair, a picnic lunch, and a foot race.

   a. Which has been most clearly described so far?

   b. Which is most likely to become important later in the story?

3. So far you know that Don expected to run in a foot race. You also know that he expected to win.

   a. Have you been told why Don expected to win?

   b. Sometimes runners expect to win because of their experience. Have you been told that Don had won other races or had even run in any other race?

   c. Sometimes runners expect to win because of the coaching and the training they have had. Have you been told that Don had had any coaching, any training, or even any practice in running?

   d. Have you been told that Don had anything except a great wish to win?

   e. What have you been told about Don that could easily keep any runner from winning?

4. So far you know that Herman also expected to run in the foot race.

   a. Have you been told that Herman also expected to win?

b. Have you been told that Herman had had any coaching, any training, or even any practice in running?

c. Have you been told that Herman had won any other races or had even run in any other races?

d. What have you been told about Herman that could help a runner to win?

5. Remember that the "today" in this story was Don's birthday, not Herman's. Remember also that Don's father had always said that Don could have anything he wished on his birthday, so long as he did not pay more than a dollar for it.

a. What was it that Don wished for more than anything else on his birthday? Was it something he could buy for less than a dollar or something he could have by winning the race?

b. Is anyone likely to win a race just because it is run on his birthday?

c. Is anyone likely to win a race just because he wishes to win it?

When Don and Herman reached the track, the girls' race was being called.

"Let's go down where we can watch the girls start," said Herman.

"Wouldn't it be better to go up to the finish line and see who wins?" asked Don.

"Maybe," said Herman, "if you care more about who wins than about what you can learn. I think I might learn something by watching the start."

"There's a lot more to running than starting," said Don.

"Yes," said Herman, "but in a hundred-yard dash, it's hard for any runner to make up for a bad start. I've been watching Mr. Jacobs, the high school coach, teach his sprinters how to start. I've been practicing starts every day in my back yard. Where do you do your practicing?"

"Oh, just wherever I feel like it," said Don. He didn't want to admit that he had done no practicing at all. He didn't want to admit that the only running he had done had been in a daydream, in which he had always won. It was a very short daydream, in which Don always leaped out of a pack of runners just before the finish line. He could not remember a single daydream about the start of a race or about running down the track. Always there was that leaping finish, that winning finish, and that was all.

No, not quite all. The daydream always went on to its best part. That was the part where Don reached up and took the barefoot silver statue from a man who had just shouted his name to the crowd.

"Come on, Don," said Herman. "You act as if you were dreaming. That's what you get for eating all that pie."

66

THE WINNER

Don followed Herman to the starting line, where ten or twelve girls were standing around. Some were waiting quietly. Some were talking.

"Look at that one," said Herman, pointing to a girl who was practicing starts. "That's Sally Jacobs. Her father is a track coach, you know. Look at that crouch! Sally really knows how to start. I'm picking her to win, aren't you?"

Don didn't want to agree. But he didn't know enough about running to disagree. All he knew about running was what he had daydreamed. His daydreams had not included Sally Jacobs — or her father — or any other girl — or any other track coach — or such things as crouches.

"Come on, girls," called the starter. "Take your places on the track."

"Watch Sally Jacobs," said Herman.

"On your marks!" called the starter as he raised his gun. Don watched as Sally Jacobs dropped lightly to one knee.

"Get set!" called the starter.

Sally rose and leaned forward. It seemed to Don that she was leaning too far forward. She must either leap ahead or fall flat on her face. If the gun didn't go off right now, she would certainly —

"Crack!" With the sound of the gun, Sally leaped out in front. Behind her, the other girls bumped each other as they tried to catch up.

"Look at that Sally go!" cried Herman.

Sally did go. She finished so far ahead of the others that she had time to stop, turn around, and watch the last two cross the finish line.

"She can really run, can't she?" asked Herman.

"She's pretty good," Don admitted. Then he added, "For a girl, she is."

"Do you think you could beat her?" asked Herman.

Don thought back to his daydream. In the pack of runners he had dreamed about, there had

68

been no girls. "Boys don't race with girls," he
said.

"No," Herman admitted, "we don't. Now we
had better go over and tell the starter we are en-
tering the boys' race. If we don't, we won't be
racing with anybody."

Twenty or more boys were ahead of Don and
Herman, crowding around the starter. As each
boy gave his name and age, the starter put them
down.

Don gave his name and age. Then, as he
stepped aside to let Herman speak to the starter,
he felt a touch on his arm. He turned to see Sally
Jacobs smiling at him.

"You're Herman Bradley, aren't you?" asked Sally. Then, before Don could say no, she went on. "Dad pointed you out to me just before my race. He told me to watch you run. He says you've got better knee action than most of his high school sprinters. So go out there and win this one, Herman. I'll be watching you."

Don gulped. "But I'm not . . . ."

"Oh, yes you are," said Sally. "If Dad says you're good, you're really good. I'm going to jog on up the track and watch your knee action when you are doing your best."

"Come on, boys," called the starter. "Take your places on the track. Line up quickly, now."

"Good luck, Herman!" called Sally. She waved to Don, turned, and jogged away.

"Knee action?" thought Don to himself as he stood at the starting line. "What does she mean by knee action? And what makes her think I'm Herman?"

All around him, other boys were hopping around, lifting their knees high as they loosened up for the race. Don hopped a few steps and then stopped. Maybe, he thought, he should not have eaten that banana cream pie, or that lemon pie, or that apple pie. Maybe he should not have had that lemonade. Maybe he should not have eaten all those sandwiches and fried chicken and salad and pickles. Maybe —

thinking about what you have read

1. People who win races do not stand around at the starting line thinking about what they should not have done. Instead they think about what they must do to win.

   a. Which boy, Don or Herman, has so far been thinking the kind of thoughts that would help him to win?

   b. Which boy has so far shown a willingness to practice that would help him to win?

   c. Which boy has tried to help himself win by not overeating?

   d. Which boy has shown enough running ability to catch the attention of a track coach?

   e. Do your answers to questions 1a-1d prove that Herman will win the race? Or do they only show that Herman is more likely than Don to win?

2. In stories about foot races, the hero usually wins.

   a. Who is the hero of this story?

   b. In real life, the winner of a race has usually earned the right to win it by working hard for what he wants. Has the hero of this story earned the right to win the race by working hard for it?

"On your marks!" called the starter as he raised his gun.

As Don dropped into a low crouch, he looked quickly right and left. Herman was somewhere out of sight.

"Get set!" called the starter. Don tried to remember how long it had been between "Get set" and the crack of the gun in Sally's race. It had been quite a long —

"Crack!" The gun caught him by surprise, much sooner than he had expected it.

Don jumped up and started running as fast as he could. There was a tight crowd of runners ahead of him and one other boy to his right. There was no one on his left.

He did not look behind him. He knew, without looking, that there was no one there.

Up ahead, the distance between Don and the rest of the pack was increasing. Was he going to be last? Not if he could help it. Not if giving everything he had would keep him from it.

He dug in and ran as hard as he could. He passed the boy on his right and caught up with one on his left. The pack was just ahead of him now. He was close enough to hear its heavy breathing and the thud of its pounding feet.

Now he was in the pack, a part of it, pounding the track with it, breathing with it. Now, for the first time, he felt at home. Being in that pack had always been a part of his daydream. Being in it now was like making his dream come true.

Up ahead, Don knew, the tape would be stretched across the track. Just before he reached the finish line, he would leap out of the pack and break that tape.

There were people lining both sides of the track. They were crowding in on him, making it

73

hard for him to pass other runners. They were shouting something he could not hear clearly.

There were a few runners still ahead of him, but for some reason they seemed to be giving up. Don almost ran into one of them, whose arms were swinging wildly as he jerked to a stop. Don saw another runner fall as he tried to stop. Still another was caught in the arms of someone at the side of the track. "Bunch of quitters!" Don thought.

Suddenly Don found himself running alone. Without even having to leap from the pack, he must have left it behind him. Somewhere up ahead he should find that tape — somewhere up there at the end of the crowd.

But wait — there was no crowd up there! Up ahead there was nothing but empty track with grass on both sides.

A voice — a girl's voice — sounded close behind him. "Herman, stop!"

So Herman was still in the race, was he? Don could hear pounding feet close behind him, gaining on him. The sound made him run harder. Then he heard a man's voice, very close to him. "Stop, boy; stop!"

What was a man doing in this race? What right did a man have to tell him to stop? Nobody could make him stop. He would run until he broke that tape, wherever it was. He would run until he won this race.

The pounding feet behind him came closer. A man, a tall man, was running beside him. An arm, a long arm, reached out and caught him. He struggled to get away, fell, got up, and was caught again. "Stop, boy, stop!" cried the man who held him.

"Let me go!" Don tried to shout, but he had no breath for shouting. "Why don't you let me go?" he tried to ask, but he had no breath left for asking. He tried to fight against the arms that held him, but he had no strength left for fighting.

"Easy, boy, easy now." The man's voice was soft, gentle, friendly. "Lie still, boy, and rest."

76

Another face, Sally Jacobs' face, appeared beside that of the man. "Do what Dad says, Herman," said Sally.

"This isn't Herman Bradley," said the man. "Herman won the race. Didn't you see him win it, Sally?"

"If this isn't Herman, who is it?" asked Sally.

"I don't know," said the man, "but I'm going to find out. This one can be a champion someday because he doesn't know what it means to give up. What's your name, boy?"

Somehow Don found breath enough to give his name. Then, still gasping, he asked, "Who are you? Why didn't you let me finish the race?"

"I'm Mr. Jacobs, a track coach," said the man. "You did finish the race, Don."

Mr. Jacobs pointed back down the track. "The finish line is back there about a hundred yards. You passed it and kept right on running."

"I didn't see the tape," said Don.

"Of course you didn't see the tape," said Mr. Jacobs. "Herman broke that tape while you were still fighting your way through the other runners. If I hadn't stopped you, I think you would have kept on running until you found a tape to break. You really wanted to win, didn't you, Don?"

Don nodded. "I wished to win more than any-thing else."

"I understand," said Mr. Jacobs. "You were a one-W runner. Someday you'll be a winner, but first you have to become a two-W runner. You don't know what that is, do you?"

"No," said Don.

"A one-W runner depends only on wishing," said Mr. Jacobs. "He might as well try to run with only one leg. It was the wish to win that kept you running after all the other runners had finished. It kept you running after your lungs felt as if they were on fire. They did feel that way, didn't they?"

"Yes," said Don. "They still burn."

"Of course they do," said Mr. Jacobs. "And your legs ached, too, but they kept right on run-ning for you because your wish to win made them go. Besides all that, you must have felt sick. Yet the wish to win kept you running."

"I felt sick, all right," said Don. "Next time I run, I'll do without that banana cream — oh, I'd rather not think about it."

"Now you're beginning to sound like a two-W runner," said Mr. Jacobs. "A two-W runner not only wishes to win. He works to win. He works by practicing and by going without foods that

78

make a runner sick. A two-W runner puts in hours, days, and weeks of practicing to get ready for just a few seconds of racing."

"I know," said Don. "That's why Herman won the race. He worked for it while I only wished for it. From now on I'm going to use that other W. You just watch me run this race next year, Mr. Jacobs. I'll work until I can run it twice as fast as I did this year."

Mr. Jacobs laughed. "Twice as fast won't be necessary. But for my sake, please run only half as far next year. Once you become a two-W runner, I don't think I can catch you."

thinking about what you have read

1. As you know, Don Bradley kept right on running after he had finished the race.

   a. Why did he keep on running? Was it to show people how far he could run? Or was it because he did not know when the race was finished?

   b. Don should have known that the race was finished when he saw the other runners stop. Instead of thinking that they had finished, he thought that they had given up. Did he then think of giving up, too?

   c. Does your answer to question 1b prove that Don's wish to win was very strong?

2. One W stood for wishing to win. The other W stood for working to win.

a. Don did not win the race, but he ran almost twice as far as Herman, who did win the race. Which boy worked harder on the day of the race, Don or Herman?

b. While Don had daydreamed about winning, Herman had practiced and had gone without things he liked to eat. Which boy worked harder before the race, Don or Herman?

c. Do the two W's, wishing to win and working to win, apply only to the training period before a race, only to the race itself, or to both?

d. Do the two W's, wishing to win and working to win, apply only to foot races?

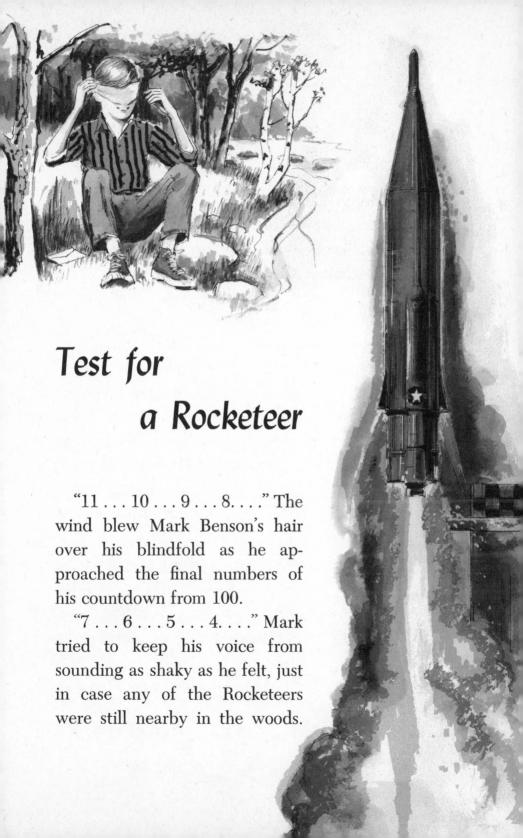

Test for a Rocketeer

"11 . . . 10 . . . 9 . . . 8. . . ." The wind blew Mark Benson's hair over his blindfold as he approached the final numbers of his countdown from 100.

"7 . . . 6 . . . 5 . . . 4. . . ." Mark tried to keep his voice from sounding as shaky as he felt, just in case any of the Rocketeers were still nearby in the woods.

"3 . . . 2 . . . 1 . . . ." It was too late to turn back now. Mark took a deep breath, said, "Zero," and pulled off his blindfold, just as he had been told to do.

He found himself in a small clearing near the bank of a fast-moving stream. The place didn't look familiar. Mark hadn't expected that it would. Very few places in Sanderstown looked familiar. After all, he had lived there just a month.

Quickly Mark unfolded the paper that the Rocketeers had given him and read the directions that he was supposed to follow.

Mark reread the directions, hardly believing his eyes. But even on a third reading the direction sheet still carried the same puzzling message and still had the secret letters LHR at the bottom.

LHR — why had he ever asked what those letters stood for? Of course, at the time it had

CROSS THE STREAM WITHOUT GETTING WET. THEN WALK ONE MILE WEST. GET YOUR NEXT DIRECTIONS OUT OF THE MOUTH OF A LION! LHR

seemed like a harmless question. Since he was interested in rockets, he had wanted to find out about the Rocketeers Club that met at the house of his next-door neighbor, Mr. Barner.

So, one afternoon he said to Mr. Barner, "Those LHR arm bands that your Rocketeers wear have me puzzled. I guess the R must stand for Rocketeers. But what does the LH part stand for?"

"I wish I could tell you, Mark," Mr. Barner replied, "but I can't. You see, the boys voted to keep the meaning of LHR a club secret. I tried to talk them out of it," he added. "I told them that if I earned the right to wear an LHR arm band, I'd want the whole world to know what the letters meant. But I guess they just like the idea of having a club secret, the same way they like having a club haircut."

"Those haircuts are another thing I've wondered about," said Mark. "How did they happen to decide on that short, flat-topped cut?"

Mr. Barner sighed. "I can't explain about the haircuts either, Mark. You'd have to know about LHR before you could understand. I'm sorry I can't do a better job of answering your questions."

"Oh, that's all right," Mark said quickly. "I didn't mean to put you on the spot. I know that

an outsider like me really doesn't have any right to be asking about club secrets." He tried to smile up at Mr. Barner as if it really didn't matter. But he could tell that Mr. Barner knew it did matter.

"You'd like to belong to the Rocketeers Club, wouldn't you, Mark?"

Mark nodded eagerly. "Dad's been teaching me about rockets for almost a year now. Just last weekend we drove to that big square field northeast of town and tested a rocket that we built. It worked, too. We have another one almost ready for testing now."

Mr. Barner looked at Mark thoughtfully. "You're younger than most of my Rocketeers, but you know as much about rockets as they know — more, in fact. Only a few of them have been out

to that field to fire their own homemade rockets.
I wonder. . . ." A worried tone crept into Mr.
Barner's voice. "I wonder if you could pass the
LHR Test."

Mark almost asked, "What's that?" but he
stopped himself in time. Everything about the
LHR Test would be a secret — of that he felt
sure. So instead he just said, "When can I try?"

The answer was "Saturday afternoon."

So here he was, this Saturday afternoon, wondering whether he had a chance to pass this LHR
Test. Of course, the Rocketeers who had blindfolded him and brought him here must have
passed it somehow. Well, if they could cross the
stream without getting wet and if they could get
directions out of a lion's mouth, maybe he could

too. Anyway, Mark decided, he wouldn't give up without trying.

1. In scene 1 you learned certain facts about Mark and the Rocketeers.

   a. Was Mark older or younger than most of the Rocketeers?

   b. Did he know more about rockets than most of them knew?

   c. What letters did the Rocketeers wear on their arm bands?

   d. Why couldn't Mr. Barner answer Mark's question about these letters?

   e. Were the Rocketeers' haircuts short and flat on top or long and wavy on top?

   f. Why couldn't Mr. Barner answer Mark's question about the haircuts?

2. You know quite a bit about what Mark thought and felt as well as what he said and did.

   a. Did he feel shaky when he approached the final numbers of his countdown?

   b. Did he try to keep his voice from shaking?

   c. Did Mark feel left out when Mr. Barner couldn't answer his questions?

d. Did he try to keep Mr. Barner from seeing how he felt?

e. After reading his direction sheet, did Mark feel for a moment that maybe he didn't have a chance to pass the LHR Test?

f. Did he decide that if all the Rocketeers had passed the test, maybe he could too?

g. Did Mark give in to his feelings or did he try to overcome them?

Mark stood on the bank, planning his pathway across the stream. A few big rocks were sticking up out of the water. Maybe he could use them as stepping stones. No, they were too far apart near the other bank. But wait — there were trees growing on that other bank, trees with low branches overhanging the stream. If he could get halfway across, jumping from rock to rock, then he could grab hold of a branch and swing himself to shore. Yes, that was the way to cross the stream without getting wet.

Mark stepped carefully out to the first rock, jumped to the second, and teetered on the third. For a moment he swayed back and forth, up on his toes with arms outstretched. Then he leaped forward to the next rock. It was wet and slippery. Mark made sure he had good footing on it before

he tried to go any farther. Now just one more
step — a long one — and he would be within reach
of the lowest branch.

"Here goes," Mark muttered. "Now!"

He was across. Quickly he grabbed for the
branch. Hand over hand, Mark swung his way
along until he could safely drop to his feet on
the far side of the stream.

Now to head west for a mile. He would follow
the late afternoon sun, Mark decided. It was
starting to set in the west. Mark walked over to
a clearing, glanced up at the sun, and then

headed down a winding path that seemed to be going in a westerly direction.

He tried to remember how many feet are in a mile. Was it 5,280? He thought so. If he took unusually long steps, he could step off about three feet at a time. So, by counting 1,760 long steps, he'd have some idea of when to start looking for a lion.

On the count of 1,280 Mark found himself coming out of the woods onto a tree-lined street. At 1,695 he came face to face with a familiar-looking old building. It was the post office that he passed every day on his way to school. It was an easy landmark to remember — with those big stone lions on both sides of the door.

All of a sudden Mark knew where to look for his second sheet of directions. He ran up to the lion on the right. Sure enough, there in its mouth was a small piece of paper on which these words were printed:

A BIRD ON A ROOF WILL POINT THE WAY.

GO

FOR YOUR FINAL DIRECTIONS LOOK INSIDE A ROCKET TO THE MOON.

Question after question ran through Mark's mind while he was reading. How could a bird "point the way"? What did the drawing mean? Certainly if there were a moon rocket on display in Sanderstown, he'd have heard about it. There must be a catch in that last sentence. Of course, there was no point in wondering about the moon rocket until he found a bird on a roof that would point the way.

Mark looked up at the roof of the post office. A lone robin hopped into sight on the very top.

He watched it fly over to a tree, back to the roof, and then out of sight around the building.

Mark shook his head. It would be silly to try to follow that bird. It changed directions every few seconds. Besides, a robin couldn't be trained to point in a certain direction.

Maybe one of the rooftops across the street held the answer. Mark's eyes traveled past a chimney, a fallen branch, a weathercock rattling in the wind, some leaves . . . wait! A bird — of course, the weathercock! It was pointing straight north.

At once Mark headed down the street in that direction. But where was he going, he wondered, and how far? He took another look at the third line on his direction sheet.

GO

Could the drawing stand for a bridge? Maybe it was meant to look like a building. All it really looked like was three blocks.

"That's it!" Mark exclaimed aloud. A passerby stared at him. "It must mean *Go three blocks.*"

At the end of the third block Mark looked for a rocket — but all he saw were houses on all four corners. There was a sale of secondhand goods going on in one front yard. "That must be where I'm supposed to find my rocket to the moon," thought Mark. "Maybe the fellows planted my final directions in an old toy rocket."

He counted the change in his pocket and then slowly approached a lady who was unloading a box of secondhand books. "Do you have any toy rockets for sale?" he asked.

"I'm sorry," she replied, shaking her head. "There are no toys at all for sale here. There are just clothes and household things and books."

"Oh." Mark sighed, wondering where else he could look for a rocket. Just as he was turning to leave, a book title caught his eye. *A Rocket to the Moon* — there it was, right on top of a pile of used books.

92

He turned back to the lady. "May I . . . may I . . . ," he started, pointing at the book and stuttering in his eagerness.

The lady was smiling. "You certainly may have your final sheet of directions. Good luck! My son is a Rocketeer," she added.

The folded paper was sticking up from between the pages like a bookmark. In a flash Mark pulled it out, opened it, and read it.

UNDER MR. BARNER'S STEPS YOU WILL FIND A HOMEMADE ROCKET.

TAKE IT INTO THE BACK YARD.

SHOW US THAT YOU KNOW HOW IT SHOULD BE FIRED.

WE WILL BE WATCHING.

IF YOU PASS THIS TEST YOU WILL EARN THE TITLE

— LHR.

Mark grinned and raced for Mr. Barner's house. This last part of the test was easy. He knew just how to fire a rocket. Dad had shown him plenty of times.

All at once Mark stopped in his tracks. He wasn't supposed to fire a rocket alone. Time and again Dad had told him that it wasn't safe.

But this time he had to do it alone. This time he couldn't ask Dad for help, even if he wanted to. Dad was out with Mother for the afternoon. Just this one time, if he was very careful, maybe Dad wouldn't mind.

The fellows in the Rocketeers Club must send up their own rockets by themselves, especially the older fellows. They must fire them right in

their own back yards, too, since that big square field where he and Dad had gone was quite a few miles away. The Rocketeers would think he was afraid if he didn't follow their directions. They might even think that he didn't know anything about rockets.

Mark walked the rest of the way very slowly, wondering what to do. As he approached Mr. Barner's house, he could almost feel the stares of all the boys who were watching him. If he didn't pass this test, he'd never be able to face any of them again.

He reached under Mr. Barner's steps and pulled out the rocket. It was small. If he set it off in the middle of the big back yard, it would

probably be safe, Mark told himself. There weren't many trees around. If anything did catch fire, he could pull over the sprinkler.

Mark walked next door to his house and went inside to think things over for a moment. There on the kitchen table was a newspaper clipping that Dad had cut out just yesterday. It was about a boy who had been badly burned firing a home-made rocket.

Accidents did happen, thought Mark — but not to him. Of course, setting off a rocket in a back yard really wasn't a good idea, especially since it was a rocket that somebody else had built. A fellow knew what to expect from his own rocket, but somebody else's — well, that was a different story.

Still, firing that rocket seemed to be what the Rocketeers expected him to do. Why had Mr. Barner let them tell him to do something this dangerous?

Mark read his direction sheet again, wondering if he had misunderstood what it said or if he had overlooked some catch in the wording. Slowly he put the paper back in his pocket, thought for a minute — and decided what to do.

1. Before you find out how Mark handled his third set of directions, you might want to think for a moment about how he handled his first and second.

   a. When he approached the stream, what did he do first — plan his pathway across or jump out onto the first rock?

   b. How did he decide which way was west?

   c. How did he keep track of how far west he was walking?

   d. Did Mark use facts that he had learned in school to help him pass the LHR Test?

   e. When Mark first spotted the robin, did he try to follow it? Or did he watch the bird, do some thinking, and then decide against following it?

   f. Time after time, did Mark think before he acted?

2. As soon as Mark read his second direction sheet, he decided that there must be a catch in the last sentence. If he had noticed that *A Rocket to the Moon* was underlined, he would have known at once what the catch was.

   a. What did the underline mean?

   b. Where did he find his final directions?

3. Mark could think of reasons for and against firing the rocket.

a. He wanted to pass the LHR Test. He wanted to show the Rocketeers that he was old enough and brave enough and expert enough to send up a rocket. Did these thoughts make him feel that he should fire the rocket?

b. Mark's father had told him never to set off a rocket alone. Mark himself thought that the whole idea of sending up someone else's rocket from a back yard was dangerous. Did these thoughts make him feel that he should not fire the rocket?

4. At the end of scene 2 some readers feel that Mark is faced with an *either-or* choice. Either he must fire the rocket or he must tell the Rocketeers that he won't fire it alone from the back yard.

a. Did Mark feel that firing the rocket would be a good choice?

b. Did he feel that saying he wouldn't fire it would be a good choice?

c. In the last paragraph of scene 2 when Mark "thought for a minute," do you think he was trying to decide between these two choices? Or do you think he was trying to come up with a third choice?

Maybe his way wouldn't be just what the Rocketeers had in mind, thought Mark, but it might be close enough. Anyway, it was certainly worth a try.

He cocked his head to one side as he added some finishing touches to the direction sheet that *he* was writing.

There! Maybe that would do it. He'd show the Rocketeers that he knew a thing or two about sending up a rocket — his own rocket — if they'd give him a chance.

Of course, they might not be willing to let him finish his LHR Test tonight. They might not want to come out to the big square field northeast of Sanderstown to see him set off his rocket. They might just say, "Sorry, Mark, you didn't fire our rocket, so you didn't pass our test, so you can't be a Rocketeer."

Quickly Mark shook that train of thought out of his head. "This *will* work," he told himself as he folded his direction sheet like a paper airplane. He carried it over to Mr. Barner's back yard and sent it sailing.

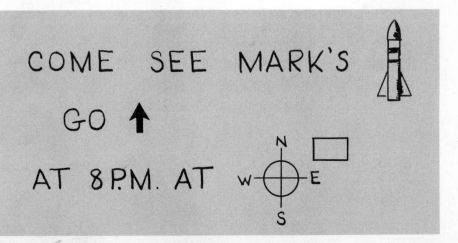

Rocketeers pounced on it from all sides. Mark stood quietly listening, waiting to hear what they would say.

For a few moments, while they were reading, he heard only low whispers. Then all of a sudden one of the Rocketeers came out with a loud cheer. The other boys started shouting too.

In a flash they were all rushing up to Mark, telling him he was all right, pounding him on the back, even turning cartwheels on the grass. Before Mark knew what was happening, the two biggest Rocketeers were pumping his hand up and down and leading him over to Mr. Barner.

"It's all right?" Mark asked excitedly. "You *will* come tonight? I *will* pass the LHR Test if I send up my own rocket?"

"Oh, we'll be there to watch all right," said the biggest Rocketeer, "but you've already passed your LHR Test — with flying colors."

"What do you mean?" asked Mark. "I didn't fire the rocket."

"Of course you didn't," said one.

"That wouldn't have been a very level-headed thing to do," said the other.

They grinned knowingly at one another as they let go of Mark's hand.

"A Rocketeer has to know what *not* to do," the older boy explained to Mark. "Any fellow who'd be stupid enough to fire somebody else's rocket alone in this yard would fail our LHR Test."

"You really had us worried when you stayed inside your house so long," said the other boy. "We've been following you all through this test, and you did so well that we were pulling for you to pass this last part."

Mr. Barner came over to Mark. "These boys have been telling me what a good, level-headed approach you took to all the problems we gave you. Your way of handling that final set of directions was the best I've ever seen. You'll make a good Rocketeer."

"Thanks, Mr. Barner." Mark grinned. "Now will you tell me what LHR means and why all the Rocketeers have flat-topped haircuts?"

"Why, Mark," Mr. Barner said kiddingly, "you must not have been listening to me very closely. I told you just now about the LH part, and your guess was right about the R. It stands for Rocketeer."

102

"LH Rocketeer?" said Mark. "I still don't get it, Mr. Barner."

"Then you'll have to find out at the barber shop," said the biggest Rocketeer. "But don't go in and tell the barber that you want a flat-topped haircut. Just tell him you're a Level-Headed Rocketeer, and he'll fix you up to look like one of us."

thinking about what you have read

1. Now you know all about the club secret and the club haircut.

   a. What did LHR stand for?

   b. Why did all the Rocketeers have flat-topped haircuts?

2. Now that you know what LHR stands for, you will have a better understanding of certain parts of scene 3.

   a. Reread page 101 and paragraphs 1 and 2 on page 102. Why did the boys grin knowingly?

   b. Near the end of the story Mr. Barner kiddingly said to Mark, "I told you just now about the LH part." In which sentence of paragraph 5 on page 102 did Mr. Barner use the words that the letters LH stand for?

103

3. Mr. Barner told Mark, "Your way of handling that final set of directions was the best I've ever seen."

   a. Of course, Mr. Barner had seen some boys fail the test. How do you think those boys handled the final set of directions?

   b. He had seen other boys pass the test, but still not do as well as Mark. How do you think those boys handled the final set of directions?

   c. What did Mark do that those boys had not done? Did he decide rightly between the *either-or* choices? Or did he think of a third choice that was better than either of the other two?

4. Judging from the things Mark had to do to pass the LHR Test, do you think that *level-headed* is closer in meaning to *sensible* or to *brave*?

Better Than a Boat

Ann Buckley tried to keep her stitches tiny and even. Dad's initials had to look just right on the handkerchief she was going to give him for Father's Day. As she was finishing the middle initial, in came her little sister Betty, looking as worried as a six-year-old can look.

"Ann!" she burst out. "Daddy *is* the best father in town, isn't he?"

"Of course, Betty."

"The best man *does* always win, doesn't he? That's what Uncle Bill says about the elections — the best man wins. That's right, isn't it?"

"Well, yes, I guess so," said Ann, giving her little sister a puzzled look.

"Then Daddy is sure to win," reasoned Betty. The worry faded from her face. "I wonder why the mailman told me not to count on it," she added, half to herself.

"Betty, what's this all about?"

The little girl smiled an I've-got-a-secret smile. "Promise you won't tell?"

"I promise."

"It's a surprise for Daddy. I'm going to give him a motorboat for Father's Day. See it." Betty pulled a crumpled newspaper clipping out of her pocket and handed it to her big sister.

Ann glanced at the heading — *Father's Day Contest* — and at the picture of the first prize, a motorboat.

"I couldn't read *all* the words on the page," said Betty, "but I understood the directions, and I did just what they said to do."

Quickly Ann read some of the small print.

106

FATHER'S DAY CONTEST

Boys and girls
in grades one through six —

Win a Father's Day
present for your dad.

In twenty-five words or less, write why
he is the best father in town. The winning father
will get a letter from the judges on the Saturday
before Father's Day.

Send your letter to the
Star Sports Store
110 Hillside Street, City.

Ann put down the newspaper clipping and stared at her little sister. Betty had come up with many a wild idea, but this was the wildest. How could a first-grader even hope to win a letter-writing contest?

"I can hardly wait for Father's Day, Ann." Betty's eyes were shining. "When Daddy gets the

107

letter from the judges, is he ever going to be surprised! I wanted to give him something special, and that motorboat is extra special."

She really does believe she'll win, thought Ann, shaking her head. Maybe if I tell her the same thing the mailman told her, I can keep her from getting disappointed. "I don't see how you can feel so sure about winning, Betty. Plenty of older boys and girls are going to be writing to the judges about their fathers, too."

"But their fathers can't win because our daddy is the best father in town, and the best man always wins." Betty's tone of voice clearly said that she thought it was stupid of Ann not to understand.

Ann wondered how she could explain to Betty that her spelling and printing and punctuation could very easily keep her twenty-five words from winning. "What did you write about Dad?" she asked.

"I'll show you," said Betty, reaching down into her pocket again. "I printed what I wanted to say on yellow paper first — just the way we do at school. Then I copied it over on white paper and gave it to the mailman. He promised to send it in for me."

From the very bottom of her pocket, Betty proudly pulled out a piece of yellow paper. There was a tear across the top, and it was spotted with strawberry ice cream, but Ann could still read the printing.

My daddy is the Nisest
Farther in town. he
is fun to pla with. he tells
funny bad time storys.
PLees send him the boat
BETTY BUCKLEY

Ann's heart sank. She had hoped that her mother or the mailman had helped Betty, but it was clear that her little sister had done this all by herself.

"Remember how much Dad liked the picture you painted for him last Father's Day," said Ann, deciding to try another approach. "He still has it hanging on the bedroom door. Why don't you paint another —"

109

But before Ann could finish, Betty was shaking her head. "No," she said flatly, starting outside again. "I'm going to give him the boat."

After Betty left, Ann reread what her little sister had written. Then she glanced at the newspaper picture of the motorboat and shook her head. Poor Betty! She'd feel terrible about having no present at all for Dad. She might even cry, and that would be awful. That would spoil Father's Day for Dad.

"I'll just have to think of a way to take care of things," Ann said to herself. The whole time she was stitching the B for Buckley on her father's handkerchief, she kept wondering what she could do. The more she puzzled over the problem, the less chance she saw of solving it.

Just as she finished stitching the initial, her mother came in.

"You'd better put that handkerchief away quickly, Ann, if you don't want your father to see it," said Mrs. Buckley. "He'll be home any minute."

Ann took one last look at her work before she folded up the handkerchief. "These initials aren't as neat and even as the initials on the handkerchiefs Dad buys at the store," she said. "I hope

110

Dad won't be ashamed to carry this handker-chief."

Her mother laughed. "Oh, Ann, what an idea! Your father can buy all the initialed handker-chiefs he wants at the store, but he can't buy what you're giving him at any store. You're giving your thought and your time and your work and your wish to please him. Those things can make any present extra special."

"Thought, time, work, and a wish to please," Ann repeated, wondering if she could make Betty understand what her mother had just said. If she could, maybe Betty wouldn't be so disap-pointed about the motorboat. Maybe Betty would even start working on some other present instead.

All at once an idea came to Ann. "Mother!" she exclaimed happily. "Dad is going to get two extra-special presents for Father's Day."

thinking about what you have read

1. Ann and Betty both looked at the same newspaper clipping, but they got two different ideas about the Father's Day Contest.

   a. Which one got the idea that the man who was the best father in town would win a motorboat?

111

b. Which one got the idea that the boy or girl who wrote the best letter about his or her father would win a motorboat?

c. Which idea do you think was right?

2. When Ann looked at what Betty had written, she felt certain that her sister could not win.

a. What mistakes had Betty made in spelling?

b. What mistakes had she made in punctuation?

c. What mistakes had she made in capitalization?

3. Let's see how Ann tried to help Betty.

a. When Ann was trying to explain to Betty why she might not win, she pointed out that many older boys and girls would write in about their fathers. Did Ann mean that those boys and girls had better fathers than Betty? Or did she mean that they were better writers than Betty?

b. Did Betty catch on to the point that her big sister was trying to make?

c. Ann reminded Betty of how much their father had liked the picture Betty had painted for him last Father's Day. How did he show that he liked the picture? (If you don't remember, reread page 109.)

d. Did Ann succeed in talking Betty into painting another picture for their father?

e. Did Ann succeed in making Betty realize that she might not win the contest?

4. Ann's mother named four things that could make any present extra special.

a. What were those four things?

b. Judging from what her mother said, would the present that Ann was making be extra special?

c. When Betty tried to win a motorboat for her father, was she putting forth her thought, her time, her work, and her wish to please?

d. Do you think the boat was the second extra-special present that Ann thought of at the end of scene 1?

For the third time in five minutes, Ann stepped out on the front porch and looked down the street. Still no sign of the mailman. Why did he have to be late on the day before Father's Day?

At breakfast Betty had proudly announced that the mailman would be bringing her present for Dad. Ann crossed her fingers for luck, hoping that what she had done would make both Dad and Betty happy.

As Ann came back in, Betty rushed outside to keep watch for the mailman. A minute later Ann heard a happy shout from her little sister. In a flash Betty was out the gate, down the street, and back with a handful of mail.

She dropped the letters on the table in front of her father. "Open all of them right away, please, Daddy," she said eagerly. "I don't know which one it is."

Ann spotted the envelope she was looking for. It was the first one Dad picked up. She held her breath.

He opened the envelope and pulled out a letter and a newspaper clipping. The clipping looked as if it had been crumpled, but now it was smoothed out and neatly folded. Across the top in heavy black newsprint were the words *Father's Day Contest.*

"That must be it," Betty whispered to Ann, dancing around excitedly.

114

Ann nodded, watching Dad's face as he read the letter. It was hard to tell what he was thinking, but she was counting on him to understand. The seconds ticked by while she waited to hear what he would say.

When he finished, he put the letter back in the envelope. Then he glanced at her and nodded. Somehow the nod said it all, everything his eyes didn't say. He understood and he was pleased.

"This Father's Day present is really extra special," said Mr. Buckley, turning to Betty. "I'd rather have this than ten motorboats."

Betty blinked. "But I thought the motorboat was first prize. What do you mean, Daddy?"

"I mean that I can get a motorboat for myself at the Sports Store if I want to. But the only way I can get the title, 'Best Father in Town,' is for you or Ann to give it to me."

"Oh, I thought the title and the motorboat went together," said Betty. "I thought the judges would give both to the same father, not to two different fathers, but I guess I was wrong. I couldn't read *all* the words on that newspaper page. You'd really rather have the title than the motorboat, Daddy?"

"I really would," he replied, smiling. "Thank you very much, Betty.

"And thank you too, Ann," he added softly, with a look that made Ann feel very important and very, very happy.

"May I see this extra-special present?" asked Mrs. Buckley, reaching for the envelope. She pulled out the letter, and this is what she read.

Dear Dad,

Betty is sure the judges of the Father's Day Contest will give you the prize. I'm not sure you'll get the motorboat, so I'm sending you Betty's letter instead. She wants you to have an extra special present from her.

Mother says work, time, thought, and a wish to please can make any gift special. Betty put plenty of these things into her letter, so I thought it could be your extra special present.

Happy Father's Day!

Ann

P. S. I think you're the best father in town, too.

1. Now you know what Ann meant when she said, "Dad is going to get two extra-special presents for Father's Day."

   a. What extra-special present did she plan for him to get from Betty?

   b. What extra-special present did she plan for him to get from her?

   c. Without realizing that she was doing it, Ann gave her father another extra-special present. It was not an initialed handkerchief, and it was not Betty's letter. But it took thought, time, work, and a wish to please. What was it?

2. Let's see how Ann and her father saved Betty from becoming disappointed.

   a. How did Ann make sure that the mailman would bring their father a present from Betty, just as Betty expected?

   b. When Betty saw her father take the newspaper clipping from the envelope, did she think the letter was from the contest judges?

   c. Did anyone tell Betty that the letter was from the contest judges?

   d. Did anyone tell her the letter was from Ann?

   e. Betty remembered that she had been unable to read some of the words on the newspaper page. So she thought she had misunderstood the part about the motorboat and the title, "Best Father in Town," going to the same man. Did Ann and Mr. Buckley let her think she had misunderstood it, even though she hadn't?

f. Were Ann and her father trying to play a trick on Betty? Or were they trying to be kind to Betty?

g. Did Betty try to give her father a present that would please him very much?

h. Thanks to Ann, did Betty succeed in giving her father a present that pleased him very much?

i. Did Ann succeed in making both Betty and her father happy?

The Combination

Charlie Reed sat down and let his feet hang over the edge of the ravine. For some reason the trail had never seemed this steep before. Here he was, only halfway up, and already his shirt was sticking to his back. Of course, his other climbs had been in cooler weather. It must have been the combination of heat and steepness, Charlie decided, that made the trail seem so hard to climb.

Well, if that was the case, he would just slow down, stop more often, and take a longer rest at each stop.

Charlie looked back down the trail. Where, he wondered, were the other fellows? Hank and Jake were always behind, but he had hoped that

Jim would turn out to be a faster climber.

Should he wait until they came along, or should he go back down the trail and see why they were not keeping up? Charlie answered the question in his mind by getting to his feet and starting down the trail. Somebody might have fallen off the trail into the ravine. If so, he should be there to help.

Charlie trotted back around the first curve in the trail. He could see another fifty yards or so, but no one was in sight. He ran that fifty yards, rounded a turn, and saw the other boys.

Jim had one shoe off. Jake and Hank were on their knees beside him.

"What's the trouble?" Charlie asked as he ran up to them.

"Nothing much," said Jim. "I've got a blister on my foot. That's all."

"Let me help you," said Charlie as he reached for his first aid kit. Then, as he took out a bandage, he asked, "What caused that blister?"

"I don't know," said Jim. "It just happened."

"I don't think blisters just happen," said Charlie. "This one could have been caused by a combination of new shoes and a hot day."

"Neat job," said Jim, as he studied Charlie's bandage. Then he pulled on his shoe, tied it, and stood up. "Can't feel a thing," he said, hopping up and down. "Thanks, Charlie. I'll do the same for you sometime."

"Fat chance," said Hank, laughing.

Jake was laughing, too. "Let me know when you get to bandage a blister for Charlie."

Jim looked puzzled. "What's the joke, Charlie?" he asked. "I thought everybody got blisters. Don't you?"

"Oh, I could get a blister, I suppose," said Charlie. "But I've never had one because I've been careful not to. Even if I did, I'd be able to take care of it." He tapped his first aid kit.

"Jim," said Hank, "when you've known Charlie as long as Jake and I have, you'll understand. Here we are, all four of us on a climb, and you are the one who gets a blister. Did you have your first aid kit with you?"

"No," admitted Jim. "I lost it a few weeks ago."

"I didn't lose mine," said Jake. "I just forgot to bring it."

"I didn't lose mine or forget to bring it," said Hank. "I just forgot to make sure it had everything in it before we started."

"Next time," said Jake, "maybe somebody besides Charlie will be prepared. Maybe so. Maybe not. But next time, and the time after that, Charlie will be prepared. You can count on that. You can always count on that."

"OK," said Jim. "Anyway, Charlie, I'm glad I could count on you today. And I'll do something for you someday. You just wait and see."

"Forget it, Jim," said Charlie. "Let's get on up the trail." Without waiting for an answer, he turned and started climbing. After he reached the first turn, he looked back. The other three, in a group, were walking along, talking. They could climb better if they didn't talk so much, Charlie thought.

He climbed on, panting a little as the trail steepened. Then he stopped to rest.

thinking about what you have read

1. Let's think about those four boys — Charlie, Hank, Jake, and Jim.

    a. Which boy was the newest member of the group?

    b. Which boy was best prepared for emergencies?

    c. Which boy seemed to do the most thinking?

d. Which boy showed the greatest responsibility for the others?

e. Which boy was most helpful to the others?

f. Which boy was alone at the beginning of the scene?

g. Which boy was alone at the end of the scene?

h. Were any of the others alone at any time during the scene?

2. Let's think about a friendly person.

a. Is a friendly person usually the kind who is helpful to others?

b. Is a friendly person usually the kind who likes to be alone?

c. Which boy in this story seemed to be especially friendly in one way but not especially friendly in another way?

Charlie tossed a pebble over the side of the trail into the ravine below. Maybe, he thought, it would have been better if he had put off resting for a few minutes. The steepest, narrowest, and rockiest part of the trail was just ahead of him. It would be good to get that part of the climb over with and then rest.

He rose, tossed another pebble into the ravine, and started up. This, he remembered, was the spot on the trail where a climber needed to be most careful. Narrowness of the trail made good

125

footing necessary. Loose pebbles made good footing uncertain. The combination meant that a climber had to be especially careful.

Charlie studied each step before he took it, then took it slowly. He was doing fine. As soon as he reached the top of this dangerous stretch, he would stop and wait for the other fellows. Somebody should warn them to watch their step. He looked back over his shoulder to see whether the others were in sight. He couldn't see much because an overhanging bush was in his way.

He stepped higher to get a better look at the trail behind him. That step forward while he was looking back was his mistake. A loose pebble under his upper foot rolled just a little — just enough to make him slip. He reached for a bush, missed it, and fell over the side of the trail.

When he stopped sliding, he was hanging to a bush a third of the way down the ravine. Rocks he had knocked loose were still rattling their way to the bottom.

He tried moving his legs. They were all right. So was the left arm. The right arm was scratched a little, but it didn't hurt. He pulled himself up and sat straddling the bush. Then he looked up at the side of the ravine above him. Could he

126

make it back to the trail?

Yes, there were rocks to hang on to. They looked solid enough. There were a few bushes, too. They looked strong enough.

He looked down. Wow! It was not so good down there. Below the bush that held him, there was little to stop a fall.

He would have to be mighty careful climbing back up. He would be. Now, was he ready to start? Again he studied the rocks and bushes between him and the trail above. He planned his path. But just as he reached for his first handhold, he heard the other fellows coming up the trail.

All he had to do now was to call out. Jake and
Hank had been waiting a long time for a chance
to help him. There was nothing they would like
better than to pay him back for the times he had
helped them. And just a few minutes ago, Jim
had promised to help him. "Just wait and see,"
was the last thing he had heard Jim say.

Charlie took a deep breath and opened his
mouth to call. Then he closed it. What should he
say? *Help?* He had never called for help. Come
to think of it, had he ever asked a friend to help
him? If so, he didn't remember it.

The three climbers were just above him now.
He could hear their shoes scraping on the rocks.

Then a pebble rolled over the edge of the trail and bounced past him, down into the bottom of the ravine.

"Hold it." That was Jake's voice, and the scratching of shoes on pebbles stopped.

"I figured Charlie would stop about here and wait for us," Jake said. "You know Charlie. He'd climb a spot like this alone and then wait to tell us to be careful."

"You're right," said Hank. "Charlie thinks he's the mother hen and we're his little chicks. I wonder why he isn't here clucking at us."

Down below, an angry mother hen ducked a pebble that somebody had thrown over the edge.

"You don't think anything could have happened to Charlie, do you?" asked Jim. "Anybody could slip on a trail like this."

"Anybody but Charlie," said Hank.

"Right," said Jake as another pebble came sailing past Charlie. "Tell me a bird forgot how to fly, and I'll believe it. Tell me a fish forgot how to swim, and I'll believe that. But don't expect me to believe that old Combination Charlie slipped and fell."

"Combination Charlie?" asked Jim. "Why do you call him that?"

Down below, Charlie Reed had the same question in mind.

"Oh," said Jake, "Charlie's always thinking a step or two ahead of the rest of us. Maybe that's why he likes to be alone. He likes to figure out things that the rest of us don't think much about. Then he comes around and tells us what he's figured out. It's usually a combination of some kind."

"Let's get going," said Hank. "If we don't, Charlie will come back down here to give us a helping hand. I can do without that."

130

"What's wrong with giving somebody a helping hand?" asked Jim. "I certainly liked what Charlie's helping hand did for my blister."

"Sure," said Hank. "Everybody likes a helping hand, and Charlie is always offering one. But he won't take help from anybody else. It's hard to be friendly with Charlie because he won't let you do anything friendly for him."

"Come on," said Jake. "Let's get on up this trail before Charlie starts looking for us down at the bottom of the ravine."

Part way down toward the bottom of the ravine, Charlie heard the crunch of pebbles above him. In four or five minutes, the three climbers would be beyond the sound of his voice. He had that much time to decide whether to let them go or to call for help.

thinking about what you have read

1. You know some things that Hank, Jake, and Jim did not know.

   a. You know that while they were talking about Charlie, he was only a few feet below them in the ravine. If you told the three climbers that, which two would hardly believe you?

b. Why would they hardly believe you? Would it be because they thought it was not like Charlie to have an accident?

c. You know that Charlie had his accident because he made a mistake. He took a step forward while he was looking back. That was a thoughtless mistake. Was it like Charlie to make a thoughtless mistake?

d. That mistake might not have been so bad if Charlie had not already made another mistake. It is a dangerous mistake to climb a steep, narrow, rocky trail alone. Was it like Charlie to make that kind of mistake?

e. Charlie was just about to call for help when he changed his mind. Was it more like Charlie to give help to someone else than to ask for it himself?

2. Down there on the side of the ravine, Charlie Reed faced a combination of problems.

a. He had to get out of the ravine, of course. If he asked for help, would the other boys know that he had heard them talking about him?

b. If he tried to climb out alone and fell, would he risk being badly hurt?

c. So far you have seen Charlie Reed as a thinker who tried to figure out the sensible thing to do. Would such a person call for help or would he risk a bad fall?

d. So far you have also seen Charlie Reed as an unusually independent boy. He could not remember ever asking anyone to help him. Besides, he had just heard himself talked about in a way that no one would like. Would such a person risk embarrassment by calling for help, or would he take a chance on a bad fall?

From somewhere deep inside him, Charlie felt hot anger rising like steam inside a kettle. What right did Hank and Jake have to talk about him like that? How long had they been calling him Combination Charlie and a mother hen?

There was something else they had said about him, too. "It's hard to be friendly with Charlie because he won't let you do anything friendly for him." What had Hank meant by that?

Was there something wrong, Charlie wondered, about not letting people help him? He had never thought about that before.

Helping others, yes, he had thought plenty about that. It was the thing to do, the friendly thing to do. But taking help from others — that was the opposite of giving help. So was that also the opposite of being friendly? Was it unfriendly to take help from others?

No, that couldn't be right! Look how grateful Jim had been about having his blister bandaged.

133

Being grateful was one way of being friendly, just as being helpful was another way of being friendly.

Suddenly Charlie remembered something else. The grateful way of being friendly had not been enough for Jim. "I'll do the same for you sometime," he had said. Now Charlie knew what Jim had meant. "Next time, Charlie, let me be the helpful friend and you be the grateful friend." That was what Jim had meant.

So being friendly was not just a one-way helpfulness. It was a two-way combination. It was giving help and taking it, too. It was not only saying, "Let me help you." It was also saying, "Thank you for helping me." The thanking was just as important a part of the combination as the helping.

"I've been cheating myself," Charlie muttered. "I've been cheating myself out of half the combination!"

He looked up the side of the ravine to the edge of the trail above him. Then he threw his head back and yelled, "Help!" It felt so good he did it again, louder. "HELP!"

Over the edge of the trail above him appeared three faces.

134

"Hang on, Charlie!" It was Jim who said that.

"We'll get you out of there, Charlie." That was Jake.

"Take it easy, Charlie!" That was Hank.

Charlie, straddling his bush, took it easy as he waited happily for a combination he was about to try. First, he would let his friends help him. Second, he would thank them for it. Now there was a combination he expected to enjoy.

thinking about what you have read

1. In this story you saw Charlie Reed face three kinds of problems. Let's see what caused those problems.

   a. Charlie fell off the trail because he stepped forward while looking back. But he would not have needed to look back if he had stayed with the other climbers. Did Charlie's unfriendly habit of doing things by himself have anything to do with his accident?

   b. Charlie was surprised and angry when he heard Hank call him a mother hen and when he heard Jake call him Combination Charlie. If he had been a friendlier person, perhaps these same things could have been kiddingly said to his face. If he had been friendly enough to take such kidding, would it have caused him to become angry?

   c. Charlie was surprised to find that he had been cheating himself out of half the combination of friendliness. Although he thought he had been friendly all along, he really had been only half friendly. Had he actually felt unfriendly or had he just not realized what being friendly really meant?

2. Charlie finally learned that being grateful is just as important a part of friendliness as being helpful.

a. Did Charlie figure that out for himself or did somebody tell him?

b. Once he knew it, would he still be an unusually good thinker?

c. Once he knew it, would the others still think of him as a leader?

d. Once he knew it, would the others still be likely to say what Hank had said, "It's hard to be friendly with Charlie because he won't let you do anything friendly for him"?

e. In learning how to become a more friendly person, did Charlie have to give up anything worth while?

f. In learning how to become a more friendly person, did Charlie gain anything worth while?

His Brother's Fan Club

Thump! Turn . . . . Thump! Toss . . . .

Was Billy going to keep that up all night, Jim Carter wondered as he squirmed farther down under his blanket.

Another toss, thump, turn — and the bunkbed headboards rattled. In the upper bunk Billy Carter rolled over, sat up, beat his pillow, and threw himself down again. As he landed, the mattress above Jim's head sagged threateningly.

"*Sandwich-spread Jim* — that's what they'll call me when they find me sandwiched in between our mattresses and squashed." Jim muttered his remarks loudly enough for his younger brother to hear, but the only answer from the upper bunk was another spell of tossing and turning.

Jim tried again, talking like a sports announcer. "It's a right to the pillow and a left to the blanket.

He's down, ladies and gentlemen. No, he's up again. Who's winning, Billy — you or the pillow?"

Still no answer. Well, it wasn't surprising. He and Billy hadn't had much to say to each other all evening — not after what had happened in the game this afternoon.

Thump! Toss, turn, thump!

Jumping-bean Billy was at it again. Jim sighed and rolled over onto his back. "Just because you missed a catch is no reason to toss and turn all night, Billy."

"That's not what you said this afternoon." Billy's answer came out slowly, in a hurt tone of voice.

"All right," sighed Jim. "So I blew my top and I'm sorry. But can you blame me? We were winning before you missed that catch — and it was such an easy catch."

Just thinking about it, Jim could feel himself getting angry all over again. There was his team — leading 3 to 2 in the last inning, thanks to the home run he had hit, and the other team already had two outs. There he was — racing across right field, scooping up the ball, and throwing it fast and straight to kid brother at third. That play should have *ended* the game. But

140

thanks to butterfingers Billy, it *lost* the game. The kid didn't even catch up with the ball until the other team was in the lead, 4 to 3.

Of course, Jim realized, it was his own fault. He never should have pulled Billy into the game. His team would have been better off with only eight players. Billy never had been and never would be good at baseball — poor kid! He'd probably go through life without ever making a home run.

Billy wants to be as good a player as you are, Jim—that's what Dad had said when Billy bought a catcher's mitt with the first money he earned on his paper route. *Billy knows that if he were good at baseball, you wouldn't look down on him.*

Remembering Dad's words made Jim squirm. He had told Dad then that he didn't look down on Billy because of baseball. He had said that he knew Billy was good at other things — helping around the house, delivering papers, lots of things. But it was easier to fool yourself than to fool the people in your family. Somehow, they seemed to know how you felt no matter what you said.

While these thoughts were running through Jim's mind, all was quiet in the upper bunk. Just as Jim was drifting off to sleep, however, Billy started tossing and turning again.

"I feel bad about missing that catch, Jim. That's why I can't get to sleep. I feel so bad about it that I hurt inside. Guess the fellows on your team think I'm not worth much."

"Aw, forget it, Billy," said Jim, forcing out a short laugh. "What do you care what they think?"

"I wouldn't care so much if . . . if . . . ."

142

"If what?"

"If you didn't agree with them. You don't think I'm worth much either."

Jim tried as hard as he could to think of an answer, but no answer came. It was almost like trying to answer Mother back when he knew — but didn't want to admit — that she was right. Finally he muttered, "Aw, go to sleep, Billy." It was the best he could do.

The next thing Jim knew, his father was shaking him by the shoulder and saying, "Time to get up, son — extra early today."

Jim rolled over, rubbed his eyes, and then blinked in surprise when he glanced at the clock. "Get up? Now? It isn't anywhere near morning."

"No, but you have a big job to do in the next few hours," said Mr. Carter, handing him a book of addresses. "You're going to deliver Billy's papers."

Jim stopped short in the middle of a stretch. "How come?" he asked, suddenly noticing how tired and worried his father looked. "What's wrong, Dad?"

"Billy woke your mother and me in the middle of the night and said he felt terrible. We called Dr. Trapp. It was his appendix, but Billy wouldn't go to the hospital until I promised to see that his papers would be delivered this morning."

Jim grabbed his father's arm. "Is Billy going to be all right, Dad?"

Mr. Carter nodded, and his tight look of worry seemed to ease a little. The lines around his mouth smoothed out as he spoke. "Dr. Trapp got Billy's appendix out before it burst. There's nothing to worry about now, but that was a close call — too close!"

"And I kept right on sleeping through all of it," said Jim, shaking his head. "Big help I am! How soon will Billy be well enough to talk on the phone, Dad?"

144

"It'll probably be all right for you to call him this evening. I know he'll want to hear how you did on his paper route."

Jim jumped out of bed and started throwing on his clothes. "He needn't worry about a thing. When Jim Carter takes over, all's well."

thinking about what you have read

1. The first few times that Jim spoke to Billy (on pages 138-140) Billy did not answer.

   a. Was Billy not answering because his feelings were hurt?

   b. Why did Jim keep trying to get his brother to answer him? Was it because he wanted to quarrel some more? Or was it because he felt that he really shouldn't have blown up at Billy?

   c. Did both brothers want to make up?

2. Billy and Jim had very different feelings about baseball and about each other.

   a. Why did Billy want to be a good baseball player? Was it because he wanted his big brother to respect him? Or was it because he liked the game?

   b. Why did Jim think so highly of himself? Was it because he was an unusually good baseball player? Or was it because he was an unusually good brother?

145

c. Why did Jim look down on Billy? Was it because Billy couldn't play baseball well? Or was it because Billy couldn't do anything well?

d. Was Jim willing to admit to his father how he felt about Billy?

e. Was Jim ashamed of the way he felt about his brother?

3. When Jim learned that his brother was in the hospital, he grabbed his father's arm and said, "Is Billy going to be all right, Dad?"

a. Does this make you feel that Jim cared for Billy even though he didn't have much respect for Billy?

b. Was Jim willing to do Billy's job?

c. Did he think Billy's job would be easy to do or hard to do?

Fixing his own breakfast took longer than Jim expected. By the time he arrived at the building where Billy picked up his *Morning Posts,* only a few of the younger boys were still there, folding their papers.

"I'm Jim Carter," he announced to one of them. "I'm taking care of my brother's route this morning," he added, expecting to be handed Billy's papers.

"So?" The boy didn't even glance up as he spoke.

"So I'd like to pick up Billy's papers," Jim answered sharply.

"What's wrong with Billy?" The boy's tone was a little friendlier.

"I'll bet he's sick," another boy chimed in before Jim could answer. "Billy would be here if he weren't sick."

"That's for sure," agreed another. "Billy never misses a day. He's never even late."

Quite a fan club Billy has here, thought Jim. When they finish talking about how great he is, I wonder if they'll remember I'm here, waiting to pick up his papers.

"You'll have to put up with seeing me instead of Billy for a while," he said. "He had his appendix out last night. Now will somebody please tell me where his papers are so I can start delivering them?"

"Over there," said the youngest boy, pointing to a pile of newspapers in the corner. "You have to fold them before you deliver them — like this." The boy made three quick folds in the newspaper, and then he tucked one end inside the other.

"Looks easy," said Jim. He made three quick folds — but they weren't even. He folded again, tucked the ends together, and put the paper down. It came unfolded.

As Jim picked up the paper for the third time, he was well aware of the smiles on the faces of his three watchers. Quickly he pushed one end inside the other, crumpling the edge. It didn't look very neat, but it did stay folded.

As he picked up the next paper, he was told, "When you finish folding one, you should drop it right into your bag. That saves time."

Billy's bag! He had forgotten it.

By now the younger boys were ready to leave.

"Is there an extra bag somewhere around here?" he asked weakly.

"No, but there's some string on the floor," said one of them. "If you tie the papers together, they'll be easier to carry."

As they walked out, Jim heard their whispers.

"Boy! Imagine forgetting his bag!"

"You'd never think he was Billy's brother."

"Everybody on Billy's route is going to be fussing about late delivery."

Within the next two hours, Jim had many a reminder of their whispers. In his first block he was met at the gate by a man who wasn't at all happy about getting his morning paper as he was leaving for work.

Farther down that block, a woman told him that she wasn't going to pay for any newspaper delivered after breakfast. "I'm sorry to see a new paperboy on this route," she said sharply. "The boy who used to deliver to me was always an early bird."

Jim just stared down at his shoes without answering her. Somehow he couldn't quite bring himself to tell the woman that he was the early bird's big brother.

At some houses on the route people stopped him to ask where Billy was. One little old lady wanted the name of the hospital so that she could send Billy a bunch of flowers. Another lady gave him a book to take to Billy. Again and again he heard what a good job his brother did.

"Billy never lets the paper get wet in the rain."

"He's a good little salesman; he talked me into taking the *Post*."

"When I pay him with a dollar bill, he always has the right change already counted out for me."

Before Jim had delivered half of the papers, the string that was holding them together broke. His poorer folding jobs came apart as they hit the ground. Refolding the papers made him later than ever. How Billy ever finished his deliveries and got back home by eight o'clock was becoming harder and harder for Jim to understand.

By the time he reached the last house on the route, he was too tired even to throw straight. His final toss was wild, and the paper landed in a flower bed that was being watered by a big sprinkler.

"Oh, no!" muttered Jim as he jumped over the fence and raced to recover his bad throw. He tried to duck the sprinkler, but it was splashing water in all directions. Big drops came raining down on him, on the paper, and on the dog that suddenly came racing across the yard.

150

A dripping, growling Jim and a dripping, growling dog both reached the newspaper at the same moment. Jim grabbed one end. The dog snapped hold of the other with his teeth and pulled.

Just then a man opened the window and called, "What's wrong out there?"

"Everything!" shouted Jim, wondering what Billy would do now.

The paper came unfolded and started to tear. Jim let go of it, and away went the dog, trailing the front page over the grass.

"Don't worry," the man said, laughing. "Spotty will bring it back to me. I guess he's just upset about not seeing his friend Billy this morning. You're new on this job, aren't you?"

Jim nodded, too tired to explain still another time about Billy and his appendix. "It's a hard job, harder than I'd thought."

The man smiled understandingly. "Following in Billy Carter's footsteps would be a hard job for any paperboy. He's worth plenty to the *Post*."

"Yes, he is worth plenty," Jim agreed, and suddenly he realized that he wasn't just agreeing with the man to be nice. He really meant it. Sometime this morning, *he* had joined his brother's fan club. If Billy ever again said, "You don't think I'm worth much," Jim knew that he wouldn't have any trouble thinking of an answer.

thinking about what you have read

1. At the end of scene 1 Jim's final words were, "When Jim Carter takes over, all's well."

    a. In scene 2 did those words turn out to be true?

    b. Reread what Jim said to the younger newsboys on pages 146-147. Do you think they liked him? Or do you think they felt he was too sure of himself?

c. Reread paragraphs 7 and 8 on page 149. At that point in the story, do you think Jim was feeling proud of Billy or ashamed of himself?

d. Did Jim find out that, when it came to handling a paper route, he wasn't as great as he thought?

e. Did you like Jim better after he stopped thinking so very highly of himself?

2. You probably realized that Jim was having a change of heart about Billy before Jim himself realized it.

a. Reread paragraph 4 on page 150. Does this paragraph make you feel that Jim was beginning to think more highly of his brother?

b. When Jim couldn't get the paper away from the dog, he "wondered what Billy would do now." At that point in the story, do you think Jim was looking down on Billy or looking up to Billy?

c. In scene 2 Jim learned something that he had not realized in scene 1. He learned that Billy was doing a hard job very well — even better, in fact, than Jim himself was able to do it. Once Jim started feeling respect for what his brother *could* do, did what Billy *could not* do seem so important?

More Than Skin Deep

Saturday morning began like any other Saturday morning for the Fentons. Instead of going to his office, Sandra's father dressed to work in his yard. Instead of going to school, Sandra dressed to go shopping with her mother.

"It's twenty minutes to nine, dear," said Sandra's mother. The statement meant much more than a stranger would have understood. It meant, "I'm ready to go shopping. Are you ready, too?" It also meant, "We have twenty minutes before the store opens." It also meant, "We have twenty minutes in which to make a fifteen-minute drive."

Sandra knew all those meanings for "It's twenty minutes to nine." She knew because she lived in a family that always did things on time but never hurried. The Fentons never had to hurry because they always started just a little early.

Mr. Fenton pinched Sandra's cheek when she told him good-by. "So long, Beautiful," he said. He always called her Beautiful, never Sandra.

At ten minutes to nine, by the clock in the car, Sandra and Mrs. Fenton were on Broadway, approaching Hill Street. Half a block away, Sandra

154

saw the light at Broadway and Hill Street change from green to red. Mrs. Fenton slowed the car, eased up to the light, and stopped. Sandra glanced to her right, up the hill that gave Hill Street its name. No cars were coming down. She glanced left. No cars were coming up the hill, either.

Sandra looked up at the light. It was still red. Then she looked right again and screamed. A car — a driverless car — was tearing down Hill Street. It looked as if it would pass in front of them. Then it suddenly swerved left and headed straight for the side of the Fenton car.

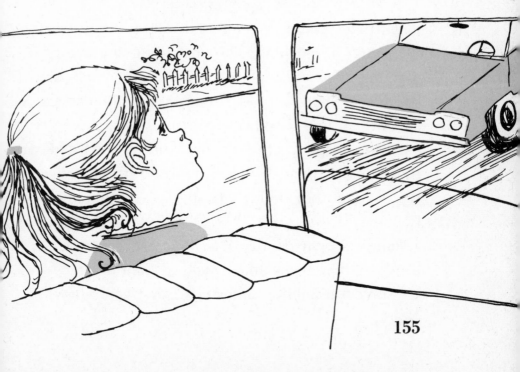

All that Sandra remembered of the crash was the sound of crashing. The next thing she knew, a young doctor was gently wrapping her face in bandages. Then she was lifted into an ambulance and rushed to a hospital.

At the hospital, other doctors and nurses lifted those first bandages. They looked at Sandra's face. Then they talked in low voices to Mrs. Fenton.

Sandra's own doctor, Dr. Bancroft, came. He lifted the bandages and looked at Sandra's face. He smiled at Sandra and said, "Don't you worry.

156

You are going to be all right." Then he turned to Sandra's mother, and his smile disappeared. "I think this is a case for Dr. Hendrix," he said.

Sandra caught the eye of a sad-faced nurse. "Don't you worry," said the nurse. "You are going to be all right." But the nurse herself looked worried.

Sandra's mother stood over her bed and stroked her hair and said, "Don't worry, dear. You aren't seriously injured." Then she turned away and wiped her eyes.

Sandra's father came. He looked strange in his garden clothes among all the nurses and doctors. He bent over Sandra's bed and whispered to her. "Hi, Honey," he said.

He had never called her Honey before. He had had only one name for her before. It was Beautiful.

Another white-coated doctor came. "This is Dr. Hendrix," said Dr. Bancroft.

Off came the bandages again. This time it was Dr. Hendrix who looked at Sandra's face. As he looked, he spoke to Dr. Bancroft. Sandra heard every word he said, but she understood nothing. Then the two doctors and her parents left the room.

Sandra lay on her back and stared at the ceiling and worried. She worried because a worried nurse had told her not to worry. She worried because too many people had told her she was going to be all right but acted as if she would not be all right.

Who was this Dr. Hendrix? Sandra had never seen him before, but he seemed to take charge as soon as he came into the room. If she really would be all right, why were so many sad-faced people whispering outside her door?

It was time, Sandra decided, to ask some questions and get some answers. She would ask the next person who came into the room.

The next person was her mother, followed closely by her father. "We've been talking with Dr. Hendrix," said Mrs. Fenton. "He's a specialist in cases like yours. He's going to —"

"What do you mean by cases like mine?" asked Sandra. "I don't even know what's the matter with me. Everybody tells me I'm going to be all right, but nobody tells me what's wrong."

Mrs. Fenton nodded. "We understand, dear. When people tell you you are going to be all right, they mean that you will feel as well as ever in just a few days. You have no broken bones or anything like that. Your worst injury is a cut. We want to make sure that it leaves as little a scar as possible. That's why we sent for Dr. Hendrix. He's going to take care of it for you."

Sandra lifted a hand to her bandages. "The cut," she said. "It's on my face, isn't it?"

"Yes, dear," said Mrs. Fenton. "It's on your right cheek."

"It will show, won't it?" asked Sandra.

"At first, yes," said Mrs. Fenton. "But after a while it should hardly show at all."

"Hardly?" asked Sandra. "Then it will show, won't it? It will always show. It will always be ugly. I'll always be ug —"

"Sandra!" Mr. Fenton spoke her name for the first time that Sandra could remember. She had never heard such sharpness in his voice before, either.

"Honey," continued Mr. Fenton, "I haven't seen our car since the accident, but I have a pretty good idea of what it looks like. No matter how it looks, I'm sure it can be made to look better. So I will see that whatever it needs is done by an expert. In the meantime, I'm not going to worry about how the car looks before the expert has finished his work. Are you?"

"No," said Sandra.

"Dr. Hendrix is an expert on cuts like yours," said Mr. Fenton. "Does it make sense to say that he is going to fail before he even has a chance to start?"

"No," said Sandra.

"Of course not," said Mr. Fenton. "That's why I wouldn't let you finish saying that you would always be ugly."

A nurse came in with a tray of tubes and bottles. "There are some tests we need to make before the operation," she said.

Sandra turned to her mother. "Operation?" she asked. "You didn't say anything about an operation."

"Dr. Hendrix is going to take care of your cheek," said Mrs. Fenton. "That's all, dear."

"Will you wait outside, please?" asked the nurse.

160

Mrs. Fenton nodded. Then she bent and kissed Sandra. "We'll see you after the doctor has finished, dear."

"So long, Honey," said Mr. Fenton.

When they had gone, Sandra turned to the nurse. "Tell me," she said. "Tell me the truth. Am I ugly?"

The nurse smiled down at her. "If you could see what I see, you wouldn't ask such a question," she said. "What I see is mostly bandages. But I also see two eyes, and one of them is turning very black. So I suppose that right now you look your worst. But you don't look ugly. I think the only people who look ugly are the ones who feel ugly inside."

thinking about what you have read

1. The first scene of this story really includes three scenes.

   a. The first four paragraphs describe an at-home scene with the Fentons. Does this scene hint that there is to be an accident?

   b. Which of the first four paragraphs seems to show that the Fentons are the kind of family in which accidents are unlikely?

   c. Which of the first four paragraphs seems to hint that this may be a story about a girl's beauty?

2. The fifth paragraph takes you to Broadway and Hill Street, just before the accident. Does this paragraph give any hint of the accident to come?

3. Paragraphs 6 and 7 describe the moment before the accident and the few minutes after it. They do not describe what Sandra felt at the moment of the accident. Was she knocked unconscious?

4. The rest of the first scene describes what happened after Sandra was taken to the hospital and before she was taken to the operating room.

a. What seemed to be Sandra's problem? Was she so seriously injured that she might not get well? Or was she so badly cut that she might always have a scar?

b. Does your answer to question 4a explain why a nurse said, "Don't you worry," while looking worried herself?

c. Does your answer to question 4a explain why Sandra's mother said, "You aren't seriously injured," but then turned away and wiped her eyes?

d. Sandra's father tried to tell her not to worry for the same reason that he was not worried about the looks of his car. But, if necessary, he could easily buy a whole new side for his car. Could he easily buy a whole new cheek for Sandra's face?

5. Before the accident, Sandra's father had always called her Beautiful. After the accident, he called her Sandra once and Honey three times.

a. Have you been told, anywhere in the first scene, that Sandra had ever really been a beautiful girl?

b. A man may call a girl beautiful because she really has the kind of beauty you see in some movie stars. He may also call her beautiful because he sees in her a beauty that is more than skin deep. Which kind of beauty would be spoiled by a scar?

c. Calling a girl Beautiful may not mean that she really is beautiful in the movie-star sense. So does not calling a girl Beautiful mean that she is ugly?

Every day, after the operation, Dr. Hendrix came to look at Sandra's face. "You're doing fine," he would say as he took off the bandage.

Sandra was more interested in how she was looking than in how she was doing. "May I see?" she asked once, when the bandage was off.

"Let's wait a while," said Dr. Hendrix. "The longer you wait, the better it will look."

Then came a day when he said, "Good news, Sandra. Half the stitches come out today. I'll take the other half out tomorrow."

"How many stitches are there?" asked Sandra.

"If I told you, you'd try to figure out the size of your wound, and you'd figure wrong," said Dr. Hendrix.

163

A few days later, Dr. Hendrix came in while Mr. and Mrs. Fenton were in Sandra's room. He took off the bandage, looked at Sandra's cheek, and nodded. "You may go home this afternoon," he said. "You no longer need a bandage."

"May I look now?" asked Sandra.

"I think you should know just what to expect before you look," said Dr. Hendrix. "It will be all right for you to touch your cheek if you wish."

Sandra slowly raised her hand to her cheek. She stared at the wall as she slowly let her fingers move lightly over the length of her wound.

"I feel the scar," she said. "It's long. It's high." Her voice trembled as she went on. "It's thick. It's rough." She burst into tears as she cried, "It's awful! It's ugly! I know it's ugly!"

Gently, Dr. Hendrix pulled Sandra's hand away from her cheek. "Let's be honest with each other, Sandra," he said. "More important than that, let's be sure that you are honest with your-

164

self. Let's begin by calling things by their right names. Put your hand up to your cheek again and tell me what you feel."

Sandra shook her head. "No," she sobbed. "I don't want to feel it again. I know what it is. It's a scar. It's a big, ugly scar."

"No, Sandra," said Dr. Hendrix. "You don't have a scar."

Sandra stared at him. "You said we'd be honest with each other!" she cried. "How can you be honest and say I don't have a scar?"

"A scar is a mark that is left after a wound has healed," said Dr. Hendrix. "What you have is a wound that is still healing."

"What difference does that make?" asked Sandra. "It's big and it's ugly."

"What is big and ugly?" asked Dr. Hendrix.

"My scar," said Sandra. Then, when Dr. Hendrix shook his head, she said, "Well, then, my wound, if that's what you want me to call it."

"That's better," said Dr. Hendrix. "I'd be worried about a scar that size, but I'm not a bit worried about that wound because I know it is healing properly. As it continues to heal, it will get smaller and smaller. The first time you look in a mirror, I don't want you to see what you

165

think is a scar that will always be there. What I want you to see is a healing wound that you know will become smaller and smaller."

Sandra put her hand to her cheek again. "It's so big, it's so —"

"Be careful with the words you use," said Dr. Hendrix. "If you keep telling yourself that your wound is big, it will look big when you see it."

"It feels awfully long to me," said Sandra.

"I don't know what awfully long means," said Dr. Hendrix. He held up his hand. "My middle finger is four inches long," he said. "My little finger is three inches long. Is your wound as long as either of these fingers?"

Sandra felt her wound again, slowly, from one end to the other. "Maybe it isn't as long as your middle finger," she said. "But it's at least as long as your little finger."

"Let's measure that wound," said Dr. Hendrix, gently placing his little finger beside it.

Sandra slowly lifted her hand to her cheek again. "Why, my sc — my wound — is only half as long as your little finger," she said.

"That's right," said Dr. Hendrix. "Your wound is only an inch and a half long. It's only half as long as you thought it was."

166

"I'm glad to know that it isn't as big as it feels," said Sandra. "Does it look very big?"

"That depends on how you look at it," said Dr. Hendrix. "Knowing how small your wound really is should keep you from seeing it as bigger than it is. Still, I think you can expect your wound to look twice as big to you as it does to anyone else."

"Is it ugly?" asked Sandra.

thinking about what you have read

1. Now you know what Sandra's parents were most worried about after the accident. Was it the effect of the accident on Sandra's health or on her appearance?

2. Dr. Hendrix could have saved time if he had handed Sandra a mirror and said, "Here, see for yourself what your wound looks like." Instead, he slowly, carefully let Sandra learn the size of her wound.

   a. Dr. Hendrix wanted to make sure that Sandra understood the difference between a healing wound and a scar. Which would grow smaller?

   b. When Sandra first felt her wound, she described it as big, thick, rough, awful, and ugly. Later Dr. Hendrix led her to describe it more exactly as an inch and a half long. One description caused Sandra to burst into tears. Was it her own exaggerated description or the exact description that Dr. Hendrix led her to make?

c. Even after feeling her wound and thinking about its size, Sandra guessed it to be twice as long as it really was. Would she be likely to exaggerate its ugliness, too?

3. So far in this story you have been told what Dr. Hendrix said but not what he thought.

a. Was he probably thinking, "I have done all I can to keep Sandra from having an ugly scar"?

b. Was he probably also thinking, "Now I must do all I can to keep Sandra from thinking that she will have an ugly scar"?

4. The scene ends with Sandra's question, "Is it ugly?" As you know, Dr. Hendrix has not yet answered that question.

a. You know the size of the wound. You also know that such a wound may be expected to grow smaller as it heals. Do you now think of it as very, or not very, ugly?

b. Remember that the wound is on Sandra's face, not yours. Is it reasonable to expect her to consider it uglier than you do?

"Whether a thing is ugly or not depends on how you look at it," said Dr. Hendrix. "When I look at the wound on your cheek, I see more than anyone else sees. I can't help seeing the deep,

168

jagged cut that you had the first day I saw you. I can't help seeing the wide, puffy, uneven scar that such a cut would have left if no doctor had taken care of you. Then I see my own work — the cleaning of the wound, the smoothing of its ragged edges, the fitting of one edge against the other, and the slow, careful stitching.

"Now I see the result, so far, of all that work. I also see the future of this wound, as the edges grow closer and closer together, until finally they form a line so thin that even you won't notice it. That line — that tiny, hairlike line — will be your scar. To me, a healing wound is not ugly. It's beautiful. But you're not a doctor, so I can't expect you to agree with me about the beauty of healing."

"Will my wound look ugly to me?" asked Sandra. "I mean while it's still healing?"

"I don't think you asked me what you really meant," said Dr. Hendrix. "What you really want to know, I think, is whether you will be ugly because you have a healing wound. The answer to that depends on you. Let's suppose that this afternoon you were going to meet the most important person in the world. You'd want to look your best, wouldn't you?"

Sandra nodded. "Of course."

"I have news for you," said Dr. Hendrix. "This afternoon you are going to meet the most important person in the world as far as your future is concerned. You are going to meet that most important person when you look into a mirror. I want you to see yourself as you would want to look if you were meeting the President himself. I want you to see yourself at your very best."

"How can I?" asked Sandra. "How can I look my best when I have this — this wound?"

"Sandra," said Mrs. Fenton, "if you were meeting the President this afternoon, you'd figure out a way to hide that wound, wouldn't you?"

"Yes," said Sandra, "I suppose so. But I don't know how I'd do it."

"I do," said Mrs. Fenton. "You are going to hide that wound from yourself in the same way you would hide it from the President. Before you look at yourself in a mirror, let's go to a beauty shop."

"Beauty shop!" exclaimed Sandra. "Mother, I don't want my face all covered with make-up from a beauty shop."

"Neither do I," said Dr. Hendrix. "Even if you were old enough to wear make-up, I wouldn't

170

want it rubbed into a wound as fresh as yours."

"I'm not thinking about make-up," said Mrs. Fenton. "I'm thinking about getting you a new hair-do, Sandra. I think you need one that —"

"I know," Sandra interrupted. "I know exactly what I need. My hair can be brought around under my right ear, like this. Then it will curl out to the front and up, like this, and be cut off in a point. It will cover most of my right cheek."

Sandra jumped up, reached for her mother's purse, opened it, and took out a mirror. "See!" she exclaimed as she looked into the mirror. "With the right hair-do, my wound won't show at all. It won't matter a bit how big it is, will it?"

"No, Beautiful, it won't," said Mr. Fenton.

"I can go now," said Dr. Hendrix. "When a patient of mine can look into a mirror and see only what she wants to see, she doesn't need me any more."

Dr. Hendrix rose, but Sandra paid no attention to him. Instead she looked past him at her father. "Daddy," she said, "this is the first time since the accident that you've called me Beautiful. Does bringing my hair down over my cheek really make that much difference?"

"That's odd," said Mr. Fenton. "All these years that I've been calling you Beautiful, you must have thought I meant the beauty of your face. Maybe I should have had that in mind, but I didn't. To me you are beautiful whenever you have a happy, sunny feeling inside. It shows in your eyes, it shows in your smile, it shows in your voice. It showed just now, for the first time since your accident, as you looked into a mirror and saw a hair-do you haven't yet had."

172

"Then a wound or a scar has nothing to do with what you call beautiful, does it?" asked Sandra.

"Not to me," said Mr. Fenton.

"It shouldn't," said Dr. Hendrix. "A scar is only skin deep. The kind of beauty that matters is much deeper than that. Good-by, Beautiful."

thinking about what you have read

1. Dr. Hendrix told Sandra that she would soon meet the most important person in the world as far as her future was concerned. Whom did he mean?

2. Mrs. Fenton suggested that Sandra get a hair-do to cover the wound. Was that like saying, "Let's not admit that you have a wound"? Or was it like saying, "Let's make the best of the fact that you have a wound"?

3. Sandra was so enthusiastic about getting a new hair-do that she paid no attention to her wound when she looked into her mother's mirror. Did she prove that Dr. Hendrix was right when he said, "Whether a thing is ugly or not depends on how you look at it"?

4. At last Mr. Fenton told why his pet name for Sandra was Beautiful.

    a. Was he thinking of the kind of beauty that can be bought in a beauty shop?

173

b. Can a girl who has a scar still have the kind of beauty that he had in mind?

c. Can a girl who feels ugly inside because she has a scar still have the kind of beauty that he had in mind?

d. Once Sandra stopped thinking, "How ugly am I?" her father could call her Beautiful. Was that because her wound suddenly grew smaller or because she suddenly stopped worrying about it?

The Getting-Even Day

"I'll get even with those fellows," Horton Burns muttered as he came in. "I'll get even!" he repeated angrily as he marched past his mother and father and ran upstairs to his room.

Just as Mrs. Burns was saying, "I wonder what that was all about," in came Pete, Horton's big brother.

"Horton's really upset," he announced.

"So we gathered," said Mr. Burns. "What happened?"

"Swiftie and Tom and I were playing basketball this afternoon, and Horton came over and

pestered us to let him play too, so we did. But he missed the basket by a mile every time he shot for it, so the fellows started kidding him."

"Didn't he at least *try* to laugh off their kidding?" asked Mr. Burns.

"No, Dad," said Pete. "He got angry right away, and then he started carrying on about getting even. Of course, Swiftie and Tom just laughed off everything he said. And they let up when they saw that he couldn't take the kidding. But by then he was too angry to have any fun."

Mrs. Burns sighed. "It's too bad there aren't any other boys of Horton's age in this neighborhood. I'm afraid your friends are a little too old for him, Pete."

"Oh, Swiftie and Tom don't mind him. But if Horton wants to run around with them, he shouldn't get his feelings hurt by every little thing they say."

"This wasn't a 'little' thing!" The Burnses looked up to see Horton at the head of the stairs. "Swiftie and Tom *meant* to be mean. Do you know what they called me, Dad?"

"No. What?"

"Hortie-Shortie. Everytime I'd miss the basket, they'd laugh, and then they'd start singsonging,

177

'Hortie-Shortie can't hit the basket.' They made a real tune out of it — dum-da, dum-da, dum dum da-dum-da."

"Aw, they didn't mean any harm," said Pete. "They've said worse things than that to me — and I've said worse to them," he ádded, chuckling. "By tomorrow they'll forget all about the blow-up this afternoon."

"I won't forget," said Horton. "I'm going to get even tomorrow morning."

Mr. Burns shook his head. "Getting even can go on and on, Horton. They called you Hortie-Shortie today, so you'll do something mean to them tomorrow — to get even. Then, day after tomorrow, they might figure that they should get even with you for the mean thing you did."

"I think getting even is a good idea," Mrs. Burns announced quietly.

"You do?" Horton blinked. He hadn't expected his mother to side with him on this point.

She nodded seriously. "You really should try to get even with Swiftie and Tom, Horton. Swiftie let you ride his bike to the store when you went to buy a new paddle for the life raft. I don't believe you've gotten even with him for that yet. Tom let you use his bicycle pump last week when

178

you wanted to inflate the raft in a hurry. Have you gotten even with Tom for that?"

"Aw, Mom," said Horton, "I should have known you weren't really taking my side."

"You don't really have a side," said Pete. "Maybe you couldn't help getting angry — we all do that — but you're being silly if you *stay* angry. Why don't you just forget about the whole thing?"

"I will — as soon as I get even."

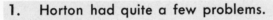

thinking about what you have read

1. Horton had quite a few problems.

    a. Were there any other boys Horton's age in the neighborhood?

    b. Did Horton try to keep up with his older brother's friends?

    c. Is it hard for a younger, shorter boy to keep up with older, bigger boys?

    d. Was Horton "one of the crowd"? Or did he sometimes have to pester the older boys before they would let him play with them?

    e. Since Horton was the youngest, shortest member of the crowd, he had a hard time keeping up with the other boys. Was he likely, therefore, to get his feelings hurt easily?

f. Once Horton started feeling hurt and angry and eager to get even, did he have any more fun with the boys?

2. Horton's family understood his problems and tried to help him.

a. When Horton's mother said getting even was a good idea, was she talking about the kind of getting even that Horton had in mind?

b. What kind of getting even was she talking about?

c. Pete knew that his friends would forget about Horton's anger very quickly. Did he think Horton should forget about his hurt feelings quickly, too?

d. In real life which is easier to forget — someone else's anger or your own hurt feelings?

3. Some people use kidding as a way of being unkind and hurtful. Some people kid unthinkingly and hurt the feelings of others without meaning to. Some people are careful never to kid about sore points, so they never hurt anyone's feelings.

a. In scene 1 which of these three kinds of people did Horton think Swiftie and Tom were?

b. Did Swiftie and Tom keep on kidding Horton when they saw that he couldn't take it?

c. Horton's mother reminded him of some kind things that Swiftie and Tom had done for him. What were those things?

d. Which of the three kinds of people described above do you think Swiftie and Tom were?

180

The next morning Horton was on his way down to the river with his life jacket and the rubber raft before the rest of his family had even finished breakfast. By 9:30 A.M. he was sitting on the raft out in the middle of the river, waiting.

He pulled his cap forward to shade his eyes and then glanced over at Shore Street. No sign of Swiftie or Tom yet, but it was still early. They'd be along. He'd have his chance to get even. This raft gave him just the chance he needed. None of the other fellows had one.

Horton jumped as he glanced over to Shore Street again. There at the corner were both of them — Swiftie and Tom. This was his chance.

He watched out of the corner of his eye as they crossed the street, spotted him, and came down to the edge of the river.

"Hi, Horton." That was Swiftie, cupping his hands around his mouth and shouting.

"How about a ride on the raft? We'll hurry back with our life jackets, Horton." That was Tom. *Horton,* they said. It was *Horton* today when they wanted a ride, but it had been *Hortie-Shortie* yesterday. He acted as if he hadn't seen them.

"Horton," Swiftie called again, louder. "Can't you hear me?"

"The people on the other side of town can probably hear you," Horton muttered under his breath as he saw a man on the opposite shore turn and stare.

Maybe he couldn't ignore Swiftie and Tom completely. Maybe he should at least wave to them. But he wouldn't take either of them out on the raft — no, not for anything. That would show them they couldn't get away with calling him Hortie-Shortie.

"Come on back to shore," Tom shouted as soon as Horton waved his hand. "Your brother Pete always lets us take turns going out on the river with him."

182

"Maybe Pete does, but Hortie-Shortie isn't about to," he said crossly, frowning at them.

"What?" shouted Tom.

"Louder!" called Swiftie. "I can't hear you."

Horton squirmed. He didn't really want to repeat what he had said. They might just laugh. "Pete'll be along later," he called out weakly. "But while I have this raft —"

The rest of Horton's words were drowned out by a sudden blast of the fire alarm. Long, short, short. Long, short, short. That meant the fire was nearby. Horton started paddling back to shore, as fast as he could go. Dad belonged to the Volunteer Fire Fighters. He'd be helping put out this fire.

Before Horton could reach the shore, the fire truck came speeding up to the corner, turned, and headed down Shore Street. Swiftie and Tom took off after it.

As soon as his raft touched the grassy river-bank, Horton jumped out and went tearing down Shore Street, not far behind the other boys.

By the time he reached the fire, the Volunteers were stringing out the crowd into a long line from

the street down to the riverbank. Women were running up and down the block, getting buckets from the neighbors.

"The hoses won't work," Horton heard a Volunteer explaining to one of the men in line. "Something must be wrong with the water pipes or our pumper. We'll have to drown this fire the old-fashioned way — with buckets of water you pass up to us from the river."

Horton spotted an open place in the line near the edge of the water. He raced down, stepped into the opening, and found himself standing between Tom and Swiftie, grabbing a heavy bucket of water from one and swinging it over to the other. What a spot to get into —just when he didn't want to talk to either of them.

Grab, swing . . . . Grab, swing . . . . Each bucket seemed heavier than the one before. Horton soon stopped worrying about talking with Tom and Swiftie. He didn't have any breath left for talking.

The buckets kept coming, faster and faster. Horton lost count of how many. Wouldn't the Volunteers ever finish putting out this fire?

At last the long-awaited shout came from the fire chief. "No more buckets. That does it."

Swiftie grabbed Horton's cap, threw it up in the air, and cheered. "Hortie," he said, "you may be a shortie, but you're a real quickie with the water buckets."

Horton dug the toe of his shoe into the ground, half angry about being called a shortie again, but half pleased about the quickie title. Before he could decide whether or not to snap back with a sharp answer, Swiftie and Tom were gone.

186

Horton stayed around to talk with his father and to watch the Volunteers reload their truck. When they finally drove away, it was time to pick up his raft and go home for lunch.

He walked back to the place where he had left the raft and found Swiftie and Tom playing ball.

"We've decided to join the Volunteer Fire Fighters when we're old enough," said Swiftie. "How about you?"

Horton didn't answer. He wasn't even listening to what Swiftie was saying. He was looking past Swiftie, up and down the riverbank. His raft! It was gone!

Swiftie and Tom must have taken it. Dad was right — getting even did go on and on. They must have hidden the raft to get even with him for the way he had acted this morning.

He marched over to them. "All right — I know you have it. Where is it?"

thinking about what you have read

1. The fire spoiled Horton's getting-even plan. But even before the fire alarm sounded, he was beginning to feel that he couldn't ignore Swiftie and Tom completely.

a. When he waved to them, do you think they felt that he was being friendly or unfriendly?

b. Why did he decide against repeating the remark, "Maybe Pete does, but Hortie-Shortie isn't about to" (page 183, paragraph 1)? Was it because he was afraid he would hurt the boys' feelings? Or was it because he was afraid he would sound ridiculous?

c. Reread pages 182-183. Did Swiftie and Tom actually hear enough of Horton's unfriendly remarks to realize that he was trying to get even with them?

2. After the fire Swiftie told Horton that he was a "quickie" as well as a "shortie."

a. Was Swiftie teasing or praising Horton?

b. Did Horton have trouble deciding whether or not to be angry about Swiftie's remark?

3. When Horton saw that his raft was gone, the first thought that popped into his mind was that Swiftie and Tom had taken it.

a. What did he think was their reason for taking the raft?

b. Think back to your answer for question 1c. Did Swiftie and Tom have any reason for wanting to get even with Horton?

c. Horton told Swiftie and Tom, "I know you have it." Did he really know that they had his raft? Or was he just guessing?

188

Swiftie and Tom stared at Horton with puzzled looks on their faces.

"Where is it?" Horton repeated.

"Where's what?" asked Tom.

"You know what." Horton's voice got louder. "Where did you hide it?"

Swiftie looked at Tom. "Did you hide something from Horton?"

Tom shook his head. "I don't know what he's talking about."

"Oh, yes you do. I left my raft right here before I ran to the fire. Now it's gone."

"I didn't take it," Tom said hotly. "You'd better not say I did! Swiftie and I just came back here a few minutes ago, and we haven't even seen it."

"Besides, we wouldn't hide it, Horton," Swiftie added. "Why should we do a mean thing like that? Pete has always been great about sharing the raft with us. And just this morning you were paddling back to shore to give us a ride when the fire truck went by."

Horton opened his mouth — and then closed it again. They must not have realized that it was the fire alarm, not their shouting, that had started him back to shore. What would be the point in telling them, now, that he hadn't been about to

give them a ride? They were already walking up and down the riverbank, looking for the raft.

"Did you leave it under one of these trees, Horton?" asked Tom.

"No, I just pulled it up on the bank."

"Are you sure it was *all* the way out of the water?" Swiftie asked.

"I . . . I think so," said Horton, trying to recall just how far up the bank he had pulled the raft.

190

Swiftie was crawling along near the edge of the water. "I can't see any marks in the mud. Of course, the raft really isn't heavy enough to leave a mark. It's so light that a few little waves could have washed it right back into the water."

"Maybe that's what happened to it," said Tom. "Maybe it just drifted a little way downstream. Or maybe somebody walked off with it," he added worriedly.

"You look up near the street, Tom," said Swiftie. "Horton and I will go down along the shoreline."

Horton glanced from Tom to Swiftie. No, they weren't just leading him on, he decided. They

really hadn't hidden the raft, and they really were trying to help him find it. He caught himself wishing he still had a raft to share with them.

"I shouldn't h a v e jumped on you and Tom about the raft," he said as he joined Swiftie at the edge of the water.

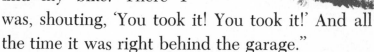

"That's all right," said Swiftie. "When a fellow gets upset, he says things without thinking. I've done it myself. I blew up at your brother Pete one time when I couldn't find my bike. There I was, shouting, 'You took it! You took it!' And all the time it was right behind the garage."

"Didn't Pete get angry?" asked Horton, wondering why his brother had never told him about this.

"Yes — about as angry as Tom got when you said we took the raft."

192

"What did Pete do to get back at you?"

Swiftie laughed. "If Pete and I worked at getting even every time one of us made the other angry, we'd never have any time for having fun together."

Horton could feel his face getting red. He wished he hadn't asked that question. He wished he hadn't worked at getting even this morning.

He and Swiftie searched farther down the riverbank in silence. When they reached the point where the river widened, Swiftie sighed and shook his head. "If the raft had drifted downstream, we'd have spotted it by now. We may as well turn back and see if Tom has had any luck."

Halfway back, Horton caught sight of Tom, waving wildly from Shore Street.

"Come here!" he shouted.

They raced up to him.

He pointed down the street — and there, hurrying toward them, carrying the raft, was Pete.

"I'm glad I finally caught up with you," Pete said to Horton. "When I came down here a while ago, there was nobody around, and the raft was up on shore. I thought you'd probably started home for lunch and forgotten to bring it with you, so I took it."

"You really gave me a scare," said Horton. "I wish you'd just left it where it was."

Pete grinned. "Well, I figured that since this was a getting-even day, it might not be too good an idea just to leave the raft around. You never know what might happen on a getting-even day."

"A getting-even day?" said Tom. "What's that?"

Pete glanced questioningly at Horton. "Didn't you . . . ?" Pete's voice trailed off as Horton frowned and shook his head.

Swiftie looked back and forth from Pete to Horton. "Now you've got me wondering too. What's this all about?"

Horton squirmed. What could he say? What would they think of him if he admitted that he had stayed angry overnight about a little kidding?

"Well," he started weakly, "on a getting-even day you pay people back for . . . for . . . ." All at once he had it, and the words tumbled out. "For all the good things they've done.

194

"Remember — you let me ride your bike to the store, Swiftie, when I needed to get a new paddle. And you let me use your bicycle pump, Tom, when I wanted to inflate the raft in a hurry. Well, since today is a getting-even day, I thought I'd pay you back by letting the two of you use the raft all afternoon."

"Boy, that's great!" said Tom. "Thanks."

"We'll have a getting-even day for you tomorrow," added Swiftie as he started down the street. "We'll be right back with our life jackets."

Not until Swiftie and Tom were out of earshot did Horton glance up at his brother.

Pete was grinning. "Hortie-Shortie," he said, "I think you grew an inch today."

1. When Horton couldn't find his raft, he made the same kind of mistake that Swiftie had made when he couldn't find his bike.

   a. What was the mistake?

   b. Was it Swiftie or was it Tom who answered Horton angrily when Horton said they had taken the raft?

   c. Did Tom stay angry at Horton long?

d. Were Swiftie and Pete the kind of friends who never got angry at each other? Or were they the kind who didn't stay angry at each other for long?

2. Horton's mother and father did not appear in the last scene, but their ideas appeared.

a. Some of the things Horton said sounded very much like the things Mrs. Burns had said earlier (pages 178-179). In which paragraphs on pages 194-195 do you find the ideas Horton had picked up from his mother?

b. When Mr. Burns said that getting even could go on and on, he had the unpleasant kind of getting even in mind. What did Swiftie say that showed that the pleasant kind of getting even could go on and on, too?

3. Reread the last sentence of the story. Did Pete mean that Horton had become taller or that he had become wiser?

Wiped Up

Before he started painting the last line on his poster, Jack Foster glanced up at the clock. The fellows in his troop would start arriving any time now, and the Scout meeting would begin in half an hour.

"S - A - L - E," he said to himself as he hurriedly went over the last four letters in bright green paint. Then he stood up to get a better look at the three posters on the floor.

"Not bad," Davey Hammel called down to him from the top of the basement stairs. "I can read your lettering from all the way up here."

"I hope plenty of people read it," said Jack. "Three posters are all I had time to make."

Ted Robinson, the new boy in the troop, came in while Jack was speaking. "Only three? That's not enough. You should have made more posters than that, Jack. Most people won't even know about our troop's toy sale if all we put up are three posters."

"But three big pieces of poster paper were all I had," said Jack. "Besides, it's taken me hours to get just these three done. You can't paint one of these big posters in five minutes, you know. Or maybe you think *you* can."

"I know I can paint faster than you can," snapped Ted, "and better too. Your posters don't have anything but lettering on them. Why

COME TO
535 BELL STREET
ON MAY 10ᵀᴴ
BOY SCOUT
TOY SALE

didn't you paint in some pictures of the toys people gave us for this sale?"

"Because I'm not the world's greatest painter, that's why," Jack growled.

"I could have painted some good pictures on them," said Ted. "It's too bad you didn't ask me for help. I can paint better than anybody else at school."

"To hear you tell it, you can do everything better than anybody else," Jack said. "After the way you acted at last week's Scout meeting, the fellows were ready to start calling you Mr. Know-It-All."

Ted's face turned red. "Then they should start calling you Mr. Know-Nothing. You don't even know how to paint your letters straight on a poster. Look at that wiggly S." Ted pointed with the toe of his shoe at the first letter of the word *SALE*.

"Don't you step on that poster!" Jack shouted.

"It couldn't look any worse if I jumped up and down on it!" cried Ted, kicking the poster aside.

"Look out!" shouted Davey as the poster hit the paint can.

Jack dived for the can, trying to keep it from tipping over. But before he could get his hands

on it, it hit the basement floor, and the bright green paint splashed out over all three posters.

"Look what you did!" cried Jack.

Ted backed away. "I . . . I didn't mean . . . ." He broke off as his voice started trembling.

Davey rushed over with some old cloths. "Quick, let's wipe up the paint. This poster on the end isn't splashed too much."

"Yes, it is!" shouted Jack, stamping over to Ted. "They're all spoiled — all because of you. I wish you weren't in this Scout troop. I wish you'd never moved here."

For a moment Ted stood as if he were rooted to the floor. Then suddenly he ducked his head, turned, and ran up the basement stairs, as fast as he could go.

A second or two later, Jack and Davey heard the back door bang shut.

Davey shook his head. "Ted shouldn't have run away like that. He should have stayed to help us clean up the paint, anyway."

"He's nothing but a know-it-all and a show-off," said Jack. "Just look at these posters. He should be put out of our troop for doing a thing like this. Say, that's an idea — let's vote him out of the troop."

"I don't think we can do that," said Davey.

"Why not?" Jack asked. "Nobody in the troop likes him. I don't see how our leader, Mr. Alexander, could like him either. You know what a noisy know-it-all he's been at meetings."

"Oh, Jack, he only came into the troop two weeks ago," said Davey. "Mr. Alexander wouldn't start disliking him after just two meetings, even though he has talked too much. Besides, he didn't *mean* to turn over the paint on your posters."

"I don't care," growled Jack. "The posters are no good now. When I tell the fellows at meeting what he did, they'll all want to vote him out of the troop."

"Mr. Alexander has never let us vote anyone out before," said Davey.

"We've never had anyone in the troop who acted like Ted before," Jack replied.

"Look," Davey began warningly, "I've been in this troop longer than you have, and I'm telling you it won't work."

"Why not?"

"Never mind why not." Davey turned away from Jack. "If I told you the real reason, you'd just get angry at me. But take my word for it — if you say anything about voting Ted out, you'll wish you hadn't."

thinking about what you have read

1. Before you read on and find out what happens at Scout meeting, let's think about what has happened so far. The trouble started from some things that the boys said to each other early in scene 1.

a. What was the first thing Davey said about Jack's posters?

b. What was the first thing Ted said about Jack's posters?

c. Which boy made Jack angry?

d. Reread paragraph 4 on page 198. What reasons did Jack give for making only three posters?

e. In paragraph 4 on page 198, was Jack trying to make Ted angry or was Jack trying to explain what he had done?

f. Did he make Ted angry?

g. Did Ted think that Jack started the quarrel?

h. Did Jack think that Ted started the quarrel?

2. Let's see why Ted acted the way he did.

a. Had he lived near Jack and Davey long?

b. At how many meetings of their Scout troop had he been present? (Read page 201 again if you do not remember.)

c. At these meetings did Ted talk too much or too little?

d. Can a new boy get noticed more easily by saying too much or by saying too little?

e. Do you think Ted wanted to make the Scouts notice and like him or notice and dislike him?

f. Did he make Jack notice and like him or notice and dislike him?

g. Did Ted mean to turn over the paint?

h. Why did Ted run away? Was it because he didn't want to help clean up the paint? Or was it because his feelings were hurt by the things Jack said to him?

3. Jack and Davey disagreed about the idea of putting Ted out of their Scout troop.

a. Why did Jack want to put him out? Was it only because Ted knocked over the paint? Or was it also because Ted had made Jack angry by saying unpleasant things about the posters?

b. Why did Davey tell Jack not to say anything about voting Ted out of the troop? Was it only because Davey thought Mr. Alexander would dislike the idea? Or was it also because of some other reason that Davey would not explain?

Jack took a seat in the back row by himself when it was time for the Scout meeting to begin. If Davey was going to keep secrets and side with Ted, he just wouldn't sit with Davey.

Some latecomers arrived ten minutes after the meeting started. As they came down the basement stairs, Jack glanced up, wondering whether Ted would be with them. He wasn't. "Good!" thought Jack. "After what he did to my posters, he *should* be afraid to come back here."

Toward the end of the meeting, Andy Watkins, the chairman of the toy-sale committee, asked Jack for the posters.

Jack stood up and angrily poured out his whole story. Davey's warnings flashed through his mind while he was talking, but he went right on anyway. "So I think we should vote Ted out of our troop," he finished. "He's made trouble every time he's been around. You can see what he did to the posters, Andy. He's just a show-off."

"Do you think this is the first time our troop has ever had trouble with a show-off, Jack?" asked Andy.

"Well, yes, I guess so," said Jack.

Andy looked questioningly at Jack. "You don't think we had any trouble with a show-off last year?"

Jack glanced around the room, wondering which of the fellows Andy had in mind. "I don't remember that anybody here made any trouble last year. Was it at the very beginning of last year before I moved here and came into the troop?"

There was a strange smile on Andy's face as he replied, "No, Jack, it was after you came into the troop."

"Well, I didn't know the fellows very well at

first. Maybe I just didn't notice . . . ." Jack's voice trailed off as one of the boys up front came out with a short laugh.

Jack could feel the eyes of everyone in the room upon him. They all seemed to be waiting for him to say something. "Well, I . . . I guess . . . ," he started weakly, wondering what he was supposed to say.

Before he could go on, Mr. Alexander said, "I've seen quite a few new boys act like show-offs at first. Of course, they don't mean to; in fact, quite often they don't know they're doing it."

All at once Jack understood, and his face felt as hot as fire. "I was the show-off last year, wasn't I?" he asked.

"Yes, at the beginning, until you stopped feeling as if you were on the outside, looking in," Mr. Alexander answered kindly.

Andy added, "At first you tried to push your way into our group by being noisy and acting like a know-it-all. But after a while you found out you could earn your way into the group by working hard and being pleasant."

Jack tried to speak lightly, but his words came out in a tight whisper. "Did the fellows want to vote me out of the troop?"

"Some of them did," said Mr. Alexander. "But Davey thought he understood why you were showing off. He had seen his little brother turn into a show-off after his mother had a new baby, but it didn't last long. As soon as his little brother stopped feeling left out, he started acting like himself again. After hearing Davey's story, the troop decided that maybe you were showing off because you felt left out. So instead of dropping you, they decided to try being friendlier."

"It worked, too," Davey broke in. "You acted better at the very next meeting."

"I think it will work on Ted also," said Mr. Alexander, "if he isn't afraid to come to our next meeting. Since he didn't come back to this one,

207

I guess he thought the whole troop would be angry with him about the posters."

"I'll fix up everything tomorrow when I see him at school," Jack said quickly. "I'll make sure he's at our next meeting. After all, we show-offs have to stick together," he added, trying to laugh.

Just then, in came Jack's mother with some freshly baked cookies for the troop. There was another woman with her, a stranger with a hat and coat on. After she introduced Mr. Alexander to the stranger, Jack heard him say, "So you're Ted's mother."

Ted's mother! Why had she come? Jack edged over, closer to the group of grownups, trying to hear what they were saying. Mr. Alexander kept his voice low as he pointed to the posters, but Jack could catch Mrs. Robinson's reply.

"But Ted didn't come back home this afternoon," she said. "He knew I was coming for him after this meeting. He asked me to drive him downtown to get a new pair of skates. Where do you suppose he could be?"

"Do you think he might have gone to a friend's house?" Jack's mother asked.

Mrs. Robinson shook her head. "He really hasn't made any friends yet."

208

"Maybe he just decided to take a long walk by himself," said Mr. Alexander.

"I hope not," Mrs. Robinson said worriedly. "In this big city I wouldn't have any idea where he'd go."

Suddenly Jack realized that he was not the only boy listening to Mrs. Robinson. The room had become very quiet, and all the boys were looking up at her.

Davey glanced at his watch. "It'll be dark pretty soon. Maybe we'd all better go out right now and start scouting around for Ted. Don't worry, Mrs. Robinson, we'll find him. After all, we are Scouts, aren't we?"

thinking about what you have read

1. When you finished the first scene of this story, you knew that for some reason Davey was holding back some facts from Jack. But you did not know either the reason or the facts. Now you know both.

   a. Why did Davey warn Jack not to say anything at meeting about voting Ted out of the troop? Was it because he was trying to keep Jack from embarrassing Ted? Or was it because he was trying to keep Jack from embarrassing himself?

   b. When Davey avoided telling Jack what had happened last year, was he trying to make Jack angry?

209

Or was Davey trying to keep from hurting Jack's feelings?

2. Jack learned some important facts at this Scout meeting.

    a. Before the meeting did Jack know that he had acted like a show-off when he first came into the troop?

    b. Before the meeting did he realize that some of the Scouts had wanted to vote him out of the troop at first?

    c. In real life does a person always know how he appears to other people?

    d. Did you realize that Jack had been last year's show-off before Jack realized it?

    e. In real life is it sometimes hard for a person to realize an unpleasant fact about himself?

    f. Did Jack, Ted, and Davey's little brother all show off because they felt left out?

    g. Did Jack and Davey's little brother stop showing off when they stopped feeling left out?

Mrs. Robinson phoned her house on the chance that Ted might have come home since she left, but there was no answer.

The boys quickly decided who would cover each block nearby. Mr. Alexander said he would go with Mrs. Robinson to drive around the blocks farther away. In no time everyone was ready to begin the search.

But just as they were starting to leave, the door opened and in rushed Ted.

"Wait!" he cried excitedly. "This'll just take a minute, and then everybody will know about our toy sale — even without the posters."

At the sight of him, Ted's mother dropped into the nearest chair, smiling weakly.

Everyone else started talking, all at once.

"Where have you been?" asked Mr. Alexander.

"You really had us worried," said Jack.

"What do you mean — everybody will know about our sale?" Davey asked. "How will everybody know?"

"Just listen a minute and I'll explain," said Ted. "After I ran out of here, I just kept on running for blocks and blocks. When I stopped, I was on a street where there were some office buildings. One of them was the newspaper office, and that gave me an idea. Maybe the newspaper would say something about our toy sale. I asked the lady in the front office, and she sent me in to talk to Mr. Cullen. He's a reporter.

"I told him all about everything — even how I knocked over the paint," Ted went on with a

211

red-faced glance at Jack. "I explained how no-body would know about our toy sale without the posters. I even told him that I was new in town and didn't know how to get back here. And you know what? He brought me back in his car. He's nice."

"Very nice," said Mrs. Robinson. "I'd like to thank him."

"You can," said Ted. "He's parking outside right now. He's going to come in and take a picture of the troop and print it with the story tomorrow. Everybody who reads the newspaper will know about our toy sale."

"Our picture — in the newspaper," Davey said excitedly. "Boy, that's great!"

"This is the best thing you could have done for the troop," said Mr. Alexander, patting Ted on the shoulder.

"And how," agreed Jack. "I've never had my picture in the newspaper before."

"Well, you will tomorrow," said Ted, still not looking Jack straight in the eye. "Here comes Mr. Cullen now."

While Ted took the reporter over to meet his mother, Jack tried to think of something he could say to Ted about the posters. "He must think I'm still angry," Jack decided. "If I show him I'm not, I guess he'll stop feeling strange around me. But how can I show him?"

Jack was still trying to decide what he should say to Ted when Mr. Cullen called the troop together. "Let's have a group shot of all you fellows with your leader," he said. "Put some of the toys you're selling on this table, and all of you gather around them."

While the boys were following his directions, Mr. Cullen spotted the poster that Davey had wiped off. "Just what we need," he said as he stood it up in front of the table. "There. That

213

poster isn't splashed badly. In fact, it looks good. It's easy to read, and it tells your story better than a headline. Where's the boy who painted the poster?"

"Right here," said Jack, stepping forward with a big smile.

"Let's have you on one side of the poster with the paintbrush in your hand," said the reporter, "and let's have Ted on the other side."

Ted came over and tried to wipe away some paint that had dried on the edge of the poster.

"Hold the poster about this high, Ted," said

214

Mr. Cullen, lifting it from the floor. "We want all the words to show up in the picture."

The reporter backed off for a good look at the group. "Fine! Now all of you say *cheese*."

"Wait!" cried Davey, feeling around on top of his head. "I think my cowlick is sticking up."

Everyone laughed. Then there was the bright flash of light. The reporter took down the names of all the Scouts, and soon he was on his way.

The boys drifted out, one by one, until just Jack and Ted were left. While their mothers talked, Jack rocked from one foot to the other,

still trying to think of the right thing to say. Ted fingered the edge of the poster and stared down at the floor.

Finally Jack stepped over and pushed some of the toys aside so he could sit on the table. "My poster got a mighty lucky break," he started, "when you knocked the paint over, Ted. If you hadn't, it never would have had its picture in the paper."

"Maybe not," said Ted. "Still, I shouldn't have upset the paint. I'm sorry I did that."

"That was an accident," said Jack. "Sure, the can was upset and a little paint was spilled, but it was easy to wipe up." Then Jack looked down at the floor and added, "Our real trouble came from the other upset."

"What other upset?" Ted asked. "Did I knock over something besides the paint can?"

"No, nothing like that," said Jack. "Our real trouble came when I got upset and spilled out some mighty mean words at you. I'm sorry about those words, Ted. I wish they were as easy to wipe up as the spilled paint."

Ted laughed. "You just did wipe up those words, Jack. You wiped them up by saying you were sorry."

216

1. Most readers do not like Ted very much when they first meet him in scene 1 of this story. But many of them feel differently about him at the end of scene 3. Let's see why they change their minds.

   a. When Ted spotted the newspaper office, he rushed inside to see whether the paper would carry a story about his troop's sale. Did this make you feel that Ted was more concerned about his own hurt feelings or about the good of his troop?

   b. Ted told Mr. Cullen all about the sale — even about his knocking over the paint on the posters. Did this make you feel that Ted was trying to show off and sound important when he talked with Mr. Cullen? Or did it make you feel that he was giving the reporter all the facts — even those facts that were embarrassing to him?

   c. In scene 1 you saw only Ted's bad points. In scene 3 you saw his good points also. Did you like Ted better at the end of this story than at the beginning?

   d. In real life do you sometimes grow to like a person that you once disliked?

2. Let's see how Jack and Ted became friends after they had quarreled.

   a. Ted happened to be the first one to say he was sorry. Did that lead Jack to say he was sorry, too?

217

b. Suppose Jack had been the first one to say he was sorry. Would that probably have led Ted to say that he was sorry, too?

c. Did it matter which one was first to say that he was sorry, so long as one of them did?

d. Early in the story, just after Ted had knocked over the paint, he did not say he was sorry. At about the same time, just after Jack had said mean things to Ted, he did not say he was sorry. At that time were both boys too angry to feel sorry for what they did and said?

e. When they were no longer angry, each boy was willing to admit that he had been wrong. Each boy was also willing to forgive the wrong that the other boy had done. Each boy was also willing to say, "I'm sorry." When a person is willing to admit wrong, to forgive and to be sorry, would you say that he is being sensible?

f. When was it easy for Jack and Ted to be sensible — when they were angry or when they were sorry?

Free From the Spotlight

Carefully Audrey Russell raised the window shade enough to let the sunlight stream into her bedroom. Then she lifted one end of the curtain, peeked out, and sighed.

219

The new neighbors were up, all right. The toddler was digging in his sandbox, and the girl Audrey's age was sitting on the porch, giving the baby a bottle of milk.

The girl's name was Gail Harper. Mom had found that out when she took a "welcome cake" over to the new neighbors the day they moved in. Audrey took another peek at Gail. She looked very pretty and very sure of herself. Everything that I'm not, thought Audrey, turning away from the window.

Just as she was crawling back into bed, her mother appeared at the door.

"Why, Audrey," she said, "I thought you'd be dressed by now. Don't be a sleepyhead. Breakfast is almost ready."

"Do I have to get up right now, Mom? I don't want any breakfast. My stomach doesn't feel right."

Mrs. Russell looked at her daughter questioningly. "Butterflies in your stomach?" she asked.

"I guess so," said Audrey. "The idea of going next door and introducing myself to a whole family of strangers scares me."

"You don't have to meet the whole Harper family at once, Audrey. Why don't you just walk over to their yard when Gail is outside and start talking to her?"

"Gail Harper will probably turn up her nose at me. She's pretty and I'm not. She knows how to take care of her two little brothers, and I've never even done any babysitting. A girl like Gail can have anyone she wants for a friend, and she isn't going to want me."

Mrs. Russell frowned. "You sound as if you don't think much of yourself, Audrey. But that's not really your trouble. Your trouble is that you think about yourself too much."

Audrey blinked. How could Mom say such a thing? She was usually so understanding.

"It would do you good to worry about someone besides yourself for a change," Mrs. Russell went on. "Why don't you try worrying about Gail Harper? She doesn't know anyone around here. She's probably very lonesome."

"All right, all right," Audrey said quickly. "I agreed last night to go over and introduce myself today, and I'll do it."

"Fine," said Mrs. Russell. "Now hurry and get dressed before you change your mind again."

Five minutes after her mother had left the room, Audrey was still staring into her closet, trying to decide what to wear. Finally she pulled out a blue dress, fresh from the cleaners, and laid it across the bed. Then she took a bath, brushed and combed her long, thick curls, got dressed, and brushed and combed her hair again.

Downstairs she looked at herself in the hall mirror and shook her head. Her shoes were not shiny enough. Her nose was too shiny. As she turned from side to side, she noticed a tiny spot on her skirt where she had spilled some milk. The cleaners hadn't taken it out completely. The Harpers would notice it right away, Audrey felt sure. What would Gail think of her?

Audrey ate breakfast very slowly.

When she finally pushed her chair back from the table, her mother glanced out the window and remarked, "Gail is in the yard right now."

Audrey nodded. With a sigh she stepped outside, and just as she did, Gail Harper and her little brother burst out laughing. Were they laughing at her? But she hadn't done anything funny. Did she look funny?

222

Audrey raised her eyes for a moment. Oh — they were laughing at the baby. They were sitting on a blanket on the grass, watching him try to crawl. One second, he was up on his hands and knees, trying to get to them. The next second, his hands went sliding out from under him and he

was down for a two-point landing on his nose and stomach, waving both arms wildly and kicking like a swimmer — but getting nowhere.

Audrey took a step toward them, then stopped. They seemed like a closed family circle. An outsider would be unwelcome, Audrey felt sure. She turned away and looked for some weeds to pull.

By the time she found a few, Mr. Harper had come out of the house and was opening his car door.

"Hop in, Gail," he called to his daughter. "I'll leave you off at the library, and you can catch the bus home later."

In a flash Gail was sitting beside him, and away they went.

Audrey watched their car until it was out of sight. When she turned to go in, her mother was standing at the back door.

"You'll try again later, won't you, dear?"

Audrey nodded.

thinking about what you have read

1. When Audrey looked at herself in the hall mirror, she noticed a tiny spot on her dress.

   a. Did she notice that spot when she first took the dress out of the closet?

b. Did she expect Gail Harper to notice it as soon as Gail looked at her?

c. Would you expect Gail to notice the spot on first glance?

d. Did Audrey expect other people to look for the things that were wrong with her, to find them quickly, and to remember them?

e. Do you think Audrey was expecting closer attention than most people were likely to give her?

2. When Audrey went outside, she heard Gail and her little brother burst out laughing.

a. Was her first thought that they were laughing at her?

b. Were they laughing at her?

c. Many shy people make the mistake of thinking that others are always watching them. Do you think Audrey was making this mistake?

3. Mrs. Russell wanted Audrey to introduce herself to the new neighbors.

a. Was Mrs. Russell asking her daughter to do something that she herself was unwilling to do?

b. Was Mrs. Russell asking her daughter to do something that Audrey was uneasy about doing?

c. Why did Mrs. Russell keep after Audrey about meeting Gail Harper? Was it because she wanted to make Audrey feel uncomfortable? Or was it because she wanted Audrey to overcome her shyness so that she could make friends more easily?

4. In paragraph 3 on page 221 Audrey talked as if she knew Gail Harper very well, even though she had not yet met Gail.

   a. Did she say that Gail could have anyone Gail wanted for a friend?

   b. Did she think that Gail would want her for a friend?

   c. Did she really know anything about Gail's wants and feelings?

   d. Was she being fair to Gail in judging her before meeting her?

When the Russells' doorbell rang shortly before noon, both Audrey and her mother went to answer it.

Their new neighbor, Mrs. Harper, was standing at the door, looking very upset. "I'm sorry to have to bother you, but I just got a call that my mother has had a bad fall. I have to go across town to her house right away, and I'm alone with the babies, and —"

"We'll be glad to help," Mrs. Russell broke in. "I'll drive you over to your mother's. While I back the car out of the driveway, you tell my daughter what has to be done for the babies."

"Thank you so much," said Mrs. Harper. Then she turned to Audrey and started explaining. "Baby Charlie will need a bottle of milk soon, warmed, of course. I was just about to hardboil an egg for Ricky's lunch when I got the call about my mother."

"I'll fix one for him," said Audrey, trying to sound sure of herself.

"Fine. He'll tell you what else he wants. He's very friendly. I usually read to him after lunch. There's a nursery-rhyme book on the kitchen table, open to 'Humpty Dumpty.' That's the one Ricky likes best."

Audrey nodded.

"My daughter Gail should be home soon," Mrs. Harper added as she hurried out to the car. "She'll take over when she gets in. Thanks again." And she was gone.

Before Audrey even reached the door of the Harper house, she wanted to turn back. Meeting Gail Harper would have been hard enough if she had done it the way her mother had suggested. But this way would be much worse. Gail wouldn't understand why she was in the house. She'd have to explain all about what had happened with Gail staring at her as if she were a burglar.

The Harpers' front door was open. As Audrey stopped to smooth her hair before going inside, she heard a cracking sound from the kitchen — and then, in a cooing baby voice, "Humpty Dumpty fell down."

Another crack.

"Poor Humpty."

Crack again.

Audrey rushed to the kitchen. There was two-year-old Ricky, taking an egg out of the carton, rolling it toward the edge of the table, and —

Audrey made a diving, sliding catch that a big-league fielder would have been proud of. Her slide started in the puddle of eggs that Ricky had already broken and ended on the other side of the freshly waxed floor.

Ricky laughed delightedly. "You play Humpty Dumpty," he crowed. "You fall down. I play Humpty Dumpty too. I fall down."

Before Audrey could stop him, he was down on all fours in the egg puddle, trying to stand on his head.

"I'm going to have to wash you from top to toe, little boy," Audrey said weakly. "I'm even going to have to wash your hair."

"Wash hair?" he asked, toddling over to her.

She nodded. Then before she realized what was happening, his sticky little fingers were in her hair.

He grabbed two long curls and started rubbing them together while happily repeating, "Wash hair. Wash hair."

Audrey tried to get up. But to succeed, she would have had to part with two handfuls of hair.

She tried to crawl away.

"Ride horsie!" cried Ricky, climbing up on her back and using her hair for reins.

Finally she lay still on the floor and waited for him to go away.

Just as Ricky let go of her hair, Baby Charlie started crying.

"Oh, the bottle!" exclaimed Audrey, remembering that the baby was supposed to be given some warm milk.

She put the bottle in a pan of water on the stove and then started trying to clean herself and the kitchen. What would Gail think of her if she should walk in now?

Before Audrey could finish picking up the broken egg shells, Baby Charlie was howling at the top of his voice, and Ricky was out of sight.

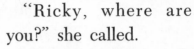

"Ricky, where are you?" she called.

He didn't answer.

Audrey carried Baby Charlie from room to room, patting him to quiet him while hunting for Ricky. "Where are you?" she called again.

"Peek-a-boo!" squealed Ricky, popping out from behind a bedroom door. "This for you," he said, coming at Audrey with an open box. It was a round box, a pretty box, a box full of bath powder.

"Oh, no!" breathed Audrey. She backed away,

clutching Baby Charlie with one hand and trying to ·shield herself with the other. The baby
wiggled and started to slip down. Audrey had to
use both hands to get a good hold on him again,
and by then Ricky had a good hold on her skirt.

With his free hand he held the box up to Audrey and shook it, saying, "For you. For you."

"Ah-choo!" said Audrey as a cloud of powder
drifted up to her nose.

"Ah-choo!" said Ricky,
dropping the box upside
down at Audrey's feet.

Powder covered her
shoes, coated her socks,
and caked against the
patches of egg white on
her legs.

Audrey hopped around,
first on one foot, then on
the other, trying to brush
off her shoes while jug-
gling the baby. "Now I
really need a bath!" she
moaned, looking at her
legs.

Just as Ricky echoed,
"Bath," Charlie came out

with another howl, his loudest yet. Audrey's ear was still ringing from it when she got back to the kitchen and grabbed his bottle out of the pan. It was steaming hot.

She put it in the sink, turned on the cold water, and rubbed butter on her burned fingers.

"Poor baby. Nice baby," she cooed to Charlie. "I know you're terribly hungry. You'll have some milk in just a minute."

Charlie's long, drawn-out waaaaaaa let her know that "in just a minute" was not soon enough. Audrey walked the floor, patting him and rocking him in her arms, but he wouldn't be quieted.

Finally the bottle was cool enough for him.

Just as she got him started on it, the phone rang. She carried him with her as she went to answer it. But there was no easy way to pick up the receiver with a baby on her left arm and a bottle in her right hand, and if she put Charlie down, he'd cry.

Another ring echoed through the house — and then another. The phone seemed to be saying, "Don't just stand there. Do something."

Audrey did something. She tried to hold the bottle under her chin for a second while she made a quick grab for the receiver. The bottle slipped. Charlie suddenly found himself without

it, and he howled. Audrey dropped the phone as
she caught the bottle and stuck it back in his
mouth. The receiver hit the floor with a bang,

and she heard a deep voice from the other end of the line shout, "Hello!"

"I have to pick up the receiver," she whispered to Charlie, who was hanging on to her hair with both hands. "Please let me put you down so I can get it."

He didn't let go.

So, still holding Charlie and the bottle, Audrey got down on her hands and knees beside the phone. Her long hair brushed against the floor as she put her mouth close to the receiver and replied, "Hello."

"Is this the home of Mrs. Harper?" the voice asked.

"Yes."

"This is Mr. Wingate, your mover. I found your missing table. Will you be home to receive it Monday morning?"

It took quite a bit of explaining, but Audrey finally made Mr. Wingate understand that she was just the babysitter and that she sounded strange because she was almost standing on her head, giving the baby a bottle, and that she had to hang up because Ricky was out of sight.

But hanging up meant taking the bottle out of Charlie's mouth. Before she could get to her feet

235

and stick the bottle back in, Ricky reappeared
and shouted above Charlie's howl, "Bath!"

"I can't give you a bath right now," she
shouted back. "I have to finish feeding Charlie
first."

Ricky raced away again, and Audrey stuck the
bottle back in Charlie's open mouth. He broke
off in the middle of a howl, and for a moment the
world seemed like a quiet place. No, not completely quiet. What was that sound from somewhere else in the house? Running water?

Audrey jumped up, shouting, "Ricky!"

No answer.

She put the bottle and Baby Charlie down in the playpen. He started crying at the top of his voice. "Poor baby," she murmured, "I'll be right back," and she raced toward the sound of running water.

As she threw open the bathroom door, there was Ricky — holding the box of bubble bath he had emptied into the basin. "Bath," he explained with a smile. "Bubble bath."

237

For a moment Audrey just stood there — with a little voice inside her crying *help* — while Charlie howled and the water ran and bubbles ballooned up from the basin.

Then she heard a girl's voice behind her, exclaiming, "Oh, my goodness!"

1. Audrey was not happy about the idea of babysitting for Mrs. Harper.

    a. Why did she want to turn back before she even reached the Harper house? Was it because she was afraid she couldn't handle the two babies? Or was it because she was uneasy about meeting Gail?

    b. Reread paragraph 1 on page 231. When Audrey started trying to clean up, was she still worrying about what Gail would think of her?

    c. Toward the end of scene 2, when Audrey was trying to talk on the phone, give Charlie his bottle, and keep track of Ricky, was she still worrying about what Gail would think of her?

2. Some babysitters would have become angry with Ricky and cross with Charlie.

    a. Did Audrey speak sharply to Ricky at any time?

    b. Did Audrey do everything she could to keep Charlie from crying?

    c. Toward the end of scene 2 was Audrey worrying about herself or about Ricky and Charlie?

238

Audrey turned to face Gail Harper. "I'll explain everything in a minute," she said, "but first please give Baby Charlie his bottle. I'll clean up in here."

While she was speaking, the phone rang.

Gail went to answer it.

Audrey turned off the water and opened the drain. As she started cleaning off the basin, she noticed that Ricky was trying to eat handfuls of bubbles.

"Not very filling, are they?" she said. "Come to the kitchen with me, Ricky, and I'll give you something that tastes better than bubbles."

By the time she had him in his highchair with milk and buttered bread in front of him, Gail was back again, carrying Baby Charlie. He was happily taking his bottle.

"That was my mother on the phone," said Gail. "She told me why you're here."

"Is your grandmother all right?" asked Audrey.

Gail nodded. "The fall gave her quite a scare, but she isn't badly hurt."

"That's good," said Audrey. In the silence that followed, she glanced down at her skirt. Spots of egg and patches of powder stood out against the bright blue cloth. She frowned, thinking about how she looked, and then that old, uneasy feeling crept up on her again.

"I'm so sorry about all this," said Gail, sounding even more uneasy than Audrey felt. "I hope you're not angry with Ricky. He didn't mean any harm, but I know you must think he's terrible."

"Oh, no," Audrey started to reply, but Gail kept on talking.

"You must think I'm terrible, too, not to have gone over to meet you. I started to this morning when I saw you weeding your yard, but I was afraid I might bother you. Besides, I was in this old dress." Gail ran her hand over her skirt and sighed. "Ever since we moved in, Mom has been after me to go over to your house and introduce myself."

"She has?"

Gail nodded without raising her eyes to look at Audrey. "I guess you won't understand this — I know it's silly — but I get butterflies in my stomach when I have to introduce myself to a stranger."

Audrey stared at Gail, hardly believing her ears. "You, too?" she said wonderingly. "I thought I was the only one who had that trouble."

240

Gail looked up. "You mean *you* feel uncomfortable when you have to meet a stranger?"

Audrey nodded. "I always feel as if there were a spotlight shining on me, showing the stranger everything that's wrong with me."

"I know just what you mean," said Gail. "I get the same feeling. I'd give anything to be able to get out from under my spotlight."

"I think I was out from under mine when you first walked in," Audrey said thoughtfully. "I didn't feel shy. I just felt glad that help had arrived. While I was thinking about Charlie and Ricky, it was just as if the spotlight were shining on them instead of on me. But when I started worrying about how I looked, I felt as if the spotlight were on me again."

Audrey stopped for a moment, trying to figure out what had happened. Then, with a smile of understanding, she added, "I guess the way to get free from a spotlight is to shine it on someone else."

thinking about what you have read

1. Audrey expected to feel uncomfortable when she met Gail Harper.

   a. When Gail walked in, was Audrey's first thought for herself or for Baby Charlie?

   b. When Gail was on the phone, did Audrey have time to start worrying about herself? Or was she too busy cleaning up and taking care of Ricky to think about herself?

   c. When Audrey was thinking about Charlie and Ricky, did she feel shy?

   d. When Audrey started thinking about how she looked, did she feel shy?

2. Gail surprised Audrey in a number of ways.

a. After Gail started talking, did Audrey keep on worrying about how she looked? Or did she become so interested in what Gail was saying that she stopped worrying about herself?

b. Was Gail as sure of herself as Audrey had expected her to be?

c. Was Gail more eager for Audrey's friendship than Audrey had expected her to be?

d. Was Gail troubled by shyness, as Audrey was?

3. In scene 3 the girls talked about their "spotlights."

a. Were these spotlights imaginary or real?

b. Did the girls feel uncomfortable when they were in the spotlight or when they were out from under the spotlight?

c. Was Audrey out from under the spotlight when she was thinking about Ricky and Charlie or when she was thinking about herself?

The Close Shave

A little more than a week ago Jerry Thompson's mother had told him he needed a haircut. She had been telling him every day since, too.

Only last Saturday Jerry's father had made his usual number one haircut joke. "What are you trying to do, Son, let your hair grow over your ears so you won't have to wash them?"

Only last night Jerry's father had made his number two haircut joke. "Son, how big a crew does a barber need to cut a crew cut like yours?" Then he had pulled gently at a handful of Jerry's hair and had laughed.

"Really, now," Jerry's mother had said. "You shouldn't tease your son that way. It would be different if Jerry put off doing everything he should do. But you know we can depend on him for everything else."

Now, as he looked at himself, Jerry knew that he could put off a haircut no longer. What had once been a crew cut was now about ready for his father's number three haircut joke. Any day now, Jerry's father would say, "Son, if your head is as fuzzy inside as it is outside, I don't see how you get any thinking done."

Jerry ran his fingers through his hair. They disappeared in it. Should he wait and give his father a chance to make the number three joke? Or should he go get himself a haircut right now? Jerry opened his dresser drawer and took out the haircut money. It had been there ever since the first day his mother had told him he needed a haircut.

Jerry put the money in his pocket. Then he called to his mother. "I'm going downtown," he said. "I need a haircut." He said it just as if his mother would think that was news.

"All right, dear," said Mrs. Thompson. "If you really think you need a haircut, go ahead and get it." Jerry's mother could always be counted on to act as if getting a haircut was Jerry's own idea. Jerry was as certain of that as he was of his father's number four joke, which always followed a haircut.

"Ho, ho!" his father would say at dinner on the evening after a haircut. "It's a boy we have as our only child. Judging by all the hair I've been seeing lately, I was beginning to think we had a girl." Then he would laugh very hard, and Jerry's mother would frown and say, "Really, now."

It was nice, being a Thompson. It was nice because you could always depend on the other Thompsons to do what you expected them to do.

It was even nice to have a teasing kind of father. Jerry had seen a few fathers who didn't have enough fun in them to want to tease their sons.

Jerry pulled on his sweater, put a clean handkerchief in his pocket, and started out the door. "Good-by, Mom," he called.

"Good-by, Jerry," she answered. And that was all she said.

Jerry had been in plenty of other homes where a boy could not say good-by to his mother without being told, "Be careful. Look out for cars. Be back on time. Put on your sweater. Get a clean handkerchief."

It seemed to Jerry that the list of last-minute things some mothers told their sons was endless. Jerry's mother never had any last-minute things to tell him, and he knew why. She expected him to do all the things she might tell him. She expected him to do them without being told.

thinking about what you have read

1. As you know, the title of this story is "The Close Shave."

   a. Can a close shave mean a smooth cutting of a man's whiskers?

b. Can a close shave also mean a narrow escape from an accident?

c. Which kind of close shave is a boy of Jerry's age more likely to have?

2. Some people are more likely than others to have close shaves of the accident kind.

a. People who are often upset and angry are more likely to have accidents than people who are calm and easygoing. Judging from the way Jerry took his father's teasing, was he a calm and easygoing kind of boy?

b. People who are unhappy are more likely to have accidents than happy people. Judging from the way Jerry felt about his life at home, was he a happy person?

c. People who are forgetful and undependable are more likely to have accidents than people who keep their minds on what they are doing. Judging from paragraph 4 on page 247, was Jerry a dependable person?

d. People who put things off until the last minute usually have to rush. They are more likely to have accidents than people who don't have to hurry because they get things done on time. Was putting off getting a haircut the only weakness shown by Jerry so far?

3. By now it should be no secret from you that Jerry Thompson would soon have a close shave of the accident kind.

248

Jerry pushed his bicycle out of the garage and swung easily onto it. He coasted slowly down his driveway, looking up and down the street for cars. There were none, so he turned right, put his head down, and pumped hard to get up speed. If he reached top speed by the time he passed the Pearson house, he knew he could coast all the way to the corner without even bothering to move his feet.

Out of the corner of his eye he caught a flash of movement in the Pearson driveway. It was close to the ground and headed toward the street. He jammed hard on the brake and skidded to a stop. Four-year-old Ernest Pearson, screaming joyfully on a tricycle, rolled out into the street ahead of him.

"Hi, Jerry!" happily called Ernest. He seemed
to have no idea how close, how very much too
close, he had come to being hurt.

"You stupid little brat!" yelled Jerry. "Who let you have a tricycle?"

"*Jerry!*" It was Mrs. Pearson's voice. It was usually a friendly, pleasant voice, but today it was sharp and frightened. "Jerry, don't blame Ernest for something that was your responsibility."

"My responsibility?" Jerry gasped in surprise. "You saw what Ernest did, Mrs. Pearson. If a car had been coming, it would have hit him."

"Just a minute, Jerry," said Mrs. Pearson, "and I'll talk to you alone. Ernest, why don't you take your tricycle into the garage? It's empty and you can ride around and around and around in there."

"Round and round?" The idea seemed to please Ernest. He started to ride his tricycle toward the garage, but he could not make it go uphill. So he got off and pushed, saying, "Round and round."

Mrs. Pearson turned to Jerry. "Now we can talk," she said. Her voice no longer sounded sharp or frightened. But it sounded more serious than usual. "You said something about a car, Jerry. No car was coming."

"But I was coming," said Jerry. "And if I hadn't stopped as fast as I did . . . ."

"Jerry," said Mrs. Pearson, "I'm glad you stopped as fast as you did, and I'm sorry I didn't

251

see Ernest in time to stop him. But that's not the point. You wouldn't have had to stop so fast if you hadn't been going too fast. You were going much too fast to be safe. That is why you almost caused an accident."

"You think *I* almost caused an accident?" Jerry's voice was filled with disbelief. "Mrs. Pearson, if I'd been riding on the sidewalk, the way the little kids do, you'd have a right to say that. But I was out in the street, where bicycles and cars belong, and where little kids and tricycles don't belong. Besides, I was the one that stopped. It was Ernest who almost caused the accident. I kept it from happening."

"Yes," said Mrs. Pearson, "you avoided an accident. But the accident that you avoided was one that you would have been responsible for. All people like you and me, who are old enough to avoid accidents, have to be responsible for people like Ernest, who aren't old enough to take care of themselves."

"Isn't it your job to take care of Ernest?" asked Jerry. "I don't see how I have anything to do with it."

"I'm going to ask you a ridiculous question," said Mrs. Pearson. "Then I think you will under-

252

stand what I mean. I
know that both your
mother and father drive
a car. Have they killed
any children lately?"

"Of course not!" said
Jerry angrily. "They are
both careful drivers."

"I told you I would
ask a ridiculous ques-
tion," said Mrs. Pearson.
"But think about it, Jerry,
and I believe you will
find it was not so ridiculous after all. Have your
parents ever skidded to a

stop to keep from hitting a child who had run
into the street in front of them?"

Jerry thought about that. "I don't remember
ever skidding to a stop when my mother or father
was driving," he said. "I guess they've been
lucky."

"Not lucky, Jerry," said Mrs. Pearson. "Good
drivers don't depend on luck to get them out of
narrow escapes. They depend on careful driving
to keep from having narrow escapes. On a street

like this, a careful driver expects a little child to do something dangerously foolish, so he drives slowly. Then he never has to skid to a stop. A car will go much faster than you can ride a bicycle, but a careful driver would not come down this street as fast as you just did."

"I guess you're right, Mrs. Pearson," said Jerry. "I'm sorry I was going so fast. I won't do it again."

"I knew I could count on you to do the right thing as soon as you knew what it was," said Mrs. Pearson. "Before long we can count on Ernest to do what is right, too. Until then, we'll just have to make up for what he doesn't know."

"I'll look out for him," said Jerry. "I'll not only ride slower, but I'll watch to see what he may be about to do."

"Good for you, Jerry," said Mrs. Pearson. "I know I can count on you to be careful. Ernest will learn to be careful, too, when he is older. He isn't stupid, you know. He's just young."

"I know he isn't stupid," said Jerry. "I'm sorry I called him a stupid little brat. I know I shouldn't have said that."

"It isn't like you to say anything discourteous," said Mrs. Pearson. "That's why I'm not angry with you. I know that you didn't mean to be dis-

254

courteous, any more than you meant to have an accident."

"But I was discourteous," said Jerry, "and I almost had an accident. If there are any stupid little brats around here, I guess I'm . . . ."

"Don't say it, Jerry," said Mrs. Pearson. "Don't say it because it isn't so. You were not the only one who made a mistake today. Ernest made one, too, you know. And so did I. If I had told him again that he should never . . . ."

"Don't say it, Mrs. Pearson," said Jerry. "If all of us hadn't made the mistakes we did, I'd be sit-

ting in the barber's chair right now, getting a haircut. Instead I've learned something."

"Instead of a haircut you've had a close shave, haven't you?" asked Mrs. Pearson.

"Oh, boy!" said Jerry. "There's a haircut joke my father never thought of. Good-by, Mrs. Pearson."

Jerry climbed on his bicycle, waved good-by to Ernest in the garage, and rode toward the barbershop — slowly.

thinking about what you have read

1. Now you know that Jerry's close shave was of the accident kind, not of the barber kind.

   a. When Jerry first got on his bicycle, he "coasted slowly down his driveway, looking up and down the street for cars." Does that quotation from the story prove that Jerry did or did not try to avoid the kind of accident in which someone might run into him?

   b. When he saw that there were no cars, "he turned right, put his head down, and pumped hard to get up speed." Does that quotation prove that Jerry did or did not try to avoid the kind of accident in which he might run into someone else?

   c. Is a person who thinks of his own safety but does not think of the safety of others as safe as he should be?

d. Is a person who thinks of his own safety but does not think of the safety of others as friendly as he should be?

2. Just after their close shave, little Ernest said, "Hi, Jerry!" and Jerry said, "You stupid little brat!"

   a. Do these two quotations prove that Jerry realized how narrowly they had escaped an accident but that Ernest did not?

   b. When Jerry called Ernest a "stupid little brat," was he putting the blame for the close shave on Ernest?

   c. If Ernest was too young to realize that he had had a narrow escape, was it fair to blame him?

3. Not all mothers would have acted as Mrs. Pearson did. Some mothers would have been so angry with Jerry that they would have scolded him. Instead, Mrs. Pearson reasoned with him.

   a. If Mrs. Pearson had scolded Jerry, would she probably have made him still more angry than he already was?

   b. Mrs. Pearson needed to prove to Jerry that he had been wrong. Would it have been easier or harder for her to do that if she had made him more angry?

   c. Mrs. Pearson was able to teach Jerry a lesson in safety because she tactfully reasoned with him. If she had scolded him, would she have taught him as much?

d. Let's see why Mrs. Pearson got little Ernest out of the way before she talked with Jerry. A four-year-old listening to Mrs. Pearson and Jerry would probably think they were arguing. He would probably take his mother's side. Would he probably be tactful?

4. You already know that Jerry was, in most ways, a dependable kind of boy. Yet he almost had the kind of accident that you would not expect of a dependable boy.

    a. After that close shave, would Jerry be just as likely to have the same kind of accident?

    b. Does your answer to question 4a prove that dependability is learned a little bit at a time?

5. Courtesy, friendliness, tactfulness, dependability, safety — you have just seen in this story how all five of these qualities can be tied up together in one happening. Is a person born with these qualities, or must they be learned, each of them a little bit at a time?

Good-by, Black Dog

Dick Grant sat on his porch steps and whistled to an old black dog. "Come here, boy!" he called. "Come here, just this once."

Dick had known that dog ever since he had lived in Parker Falls. He had whistled to it and called to it almost every day.

Now, as always before, the dog walked slowly past Dick's house. As always, it looked straight
ahead. As always, it paid no attention to a whistle
or a call. It acted as if it owned the street, the
neighborhood, and the whole world, all by itself.
Dick had never heard it bark or growl. He had
never seen it chase a cat or a car or another dog.
He had never seen it wag its tail.

"Come here, boy," Dick called, snapping his
fingers. "This is your last chance. I'm moving
away tomorrow."

The black dog walked slowly on without turning its head. When it had passed, Dick turned his
attention to the two brown pups across the street.
What a difference there was between those wiggly
bundles of friendliness and the old black dog!

The two pups stood at the edge of their yard,
facing Dick. Their bodies were wiggling and their
tails were wagging as they leaned toward him.
Just one low whistle, just one call, or just one
snap of the fingers was all they needed. Then they
would tumble over each other in their dash
across the street.

Dick started to whistle to them. Then he
stopped. Those were Sid Nelson's pups, and Sid
Nelson was no longer his friend. It would never

do for Sid to catch Dick being friendly with those pups. That would be too much like old times, when Sid and Dick had been pals.

A sniffle sounded from the porch swing. Why, Dick wondered, was Vera, his older sister, crying?

Oh, he knew her reason well enough. She didn't want to move away from Parker Falls, where the Grants had lived for the last few years. But knowing her reason did not help Dick to understand it. To his way of thinking, anybody should be glad to leave Parker Falls.

"I can't help crying," Vera said. "Everybody has been so nice to me that I fill up with tears every time somebody tells me good-by. Then when people tell me how much they like me and how much they'll miss me, I break down."

"The trouble with you," said Dick, "is that you believe what people say. Nobody in Parker Falls really likes us, and nobody is going to miss us. People are being nice because they are glad we are leaving."

"That's not so, Dick," said Vera. "It'll take years for us to make as many friends in Colton as we have here."

"Not for me," said Dick. "I'll have more friends in Colton by tomorrow night than I've got here.

If I make just one friend in Colton, I'll be that much ahead. I don't have one friend here."

"Dick, you don't mean that," said Vera. "What about all the Scouts in your troop? They're all your friends, aren't they?"

"I used to think so," said Dick, "but not any more. Not one of those kids really deserves to be a Scout. Not one of them lives up to the Scout Law. Not one of them even lives up to the first part of it."

"I remember helping you when you were learning the Scout Law," said Vera. "There are several parts to it, aren't there?"

"Yes," said Dick. "Twelve."

"I remember the first part," said Vera. "It's that a Scout is trustworthy, isn't it?"

"That's right," said Dick. "Anybody that isn't trustworthy has no right to be a Scout."

"I'm not so sure about that," said Vera. "It takes a long time to learn how to be trustworthy. I should think that a boy who is trying to learn how to be trustworthy would have a right to be a Scout. Don't forget that being trustworthy takes in a lot of things. If a person is fair, honest, truthful, dependable, and reasonable, you'd call him trustworthy, wouldn't you?"

"I've never thought about all those words," said Dick. "I call a fellow trustworthy if I can count on him, that's all."

"If you can count on him to do what?" asked Vera.

"If I can count on him, that's all," said Dick.

"You aren't telling me what you mean, but I'm afraid I know," said Vera. "You want to count on people to do what you would do if you were in their place, don't you?"

"That's right," said Dick. "What's wrong with that?"

"People are different," said Vera. "You can't expect them to like the same things you like or to do the same things you do. If I limited my friends to those people who are just like me, I wouldn't have many friends."

"I do what's right," said Dick, "and I expect my friends to do the same. The trouble is that nobody in Parker Falls can be counted on to do what's right."

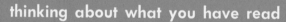

thinking about what you have read

1. Dick saw an old black dog and two brown pups.

   a. Did the old black dog do what Dick had learned to expect it to do?

b. Did the two pups do what Dick had learned to expect them to do?

c. Could Dick count on the old black dog to be unfriendly just as much as he could count on the pups to be friendly?

d. Dick said, "I call a fellow trustworthy if I can count on him, that's all." Does such a statement make much sense if you don't know what it is you can count on someone to do?

2. Vera was afraid that she would have a hard time making friends in Colton.

    a. Had she made many friends in Parker Falls?

    b. Is a person who has made many friends in one place likely to make many friends in another place?

3. Dick was sure that he would easily make friends in Colton.

    a. Had he made many friends in Parker Falls?

    b. Is a person who has made few friends in one place likely to make few friends in another place?

4. Was it kind and fair and reasonable of Dick to say that nobody in Parker Falls could be counted on to do what was right?

5. Vera said that being trustworthy meant being "fair, honest, truthful, dependable, and reasonable."

    a. According to those meanings, was Dick himself as trustworthy as he expected other people to be?

Dick and Vera looked up as a door slammed in the house across the street. Sid Nelson came out of the house and whistled to his pups. They ran to him and jumped up to lick his hand.

"There's somebody you can count on, Dick," said Vera. "You can always count on your pal Sid to do what's right, can't you?"

"Sid is no pal of mine," said Dick. "Not any more, anyway. I'm going inside. I don't want to talk to him."

As Dick rose from the steps and turned toward the door, Sid called to him. "Hey, Dick! Wait a minute."

Dick did not turn his head as he went into his house and closed the door behind him. He was careful to close the door quietly, not to slam it.

He did not like people who slammed doors.

After he had closed the door, Dick put his ear against it and listened.

"Hello, Sid," he heard Vera say quietly, so he knew that Sid had crossed the street. "Dick must have been thinking so hard about something that he didn't hear you call to him. Go right on in if you want to see him."

"I'd better not," said Sid. There was a pause, as if Sid were walking away. Then Dick heard his voice again. "Vera, is it true that you are moving away?"

"Yes, Sid," said Vera. "Tomorrow."

"I'm sorry," Sid said. "You know," he added, "Dick and I — we —"

"I know," said Vera. "You and Dick have been friends for a long time. Maybe you can come to visit us in Colton. It's not too far from Parker Falls."

"It's pretty far," said Sid. "Well, no, it's not so far, either. It's just — well — I don't know."

There was another pause, an uncomfortable pause. Then Sid said, "Vera, just in case I don't get to see Dick before he leaves, will you tell him something for me?"

"Of course, Sid."

"Tell him," Sid began. Then he stopped. Then he began again. "Tell him good-by and good luck — lots and lots of luck. Tell him I'm sorry — no, just tell him lots of luck."

"I'll tell him," said Vera. "But I think it would be better if you told him yourself."

"I'd like to tell him," Sid answered, "but I'm not sure he'd listen to me. He — well, Dick shuts me out. I don't know what I did that makes him shut me out, but whatever it was, I'm sorry. If he ever needs a friend, he can count on me. Tell him that, will you, Vera?"

"I'll tell him," said Vera. "I'll tell him right now. Good-by, Sid."

Dick pulled his ear away from the door and hurried toward his room. He was in his room when he heard the front door close. He had a book in his hand and was staring at it when Vera entered.

"Now, when did you start reading upside down?" she asked.

Dick turned his book right side up. "I just picked it up," he said. "I hadn't started reading."

"Of course not," said Vera. "You had just started pretending to read, that's all. That's not the only pretending you've been doing, either. I

268

think it's about time you stopped pretending that you are the faultless one who passes judgment on all others. What do you have against Sid?"

"I found out I couldn't count on him," said Dick.

"What was it you couldn't count on him to do?" asked Vera.

"It doesn't matter what it was," said Dick. "If you can't count on somebody, you just can't count on him."

"Do you know what Sid just told me?" asked Vera. "He just said that if you ever needed a friend, you could count on him."

"That was easy enough to say," said Dick. "It isn't so easy to believe."

"Because you can't count on him?" asked Vera.

"That's right," said Dick.

"Can people count on you?" asked Vera.

"They certainly can," said Dick. "I live up to the Scout Law."

"I suppose you mean the part about being trustworthy," said Vera. "What about the parts that say a Scout is friendly, courteous, and kind? Do you think people can count on you to be friendly, courteous, and kind?"

"If people are friendly, courteous, and kind themselves, they can count on me to be the same," said Dick.

"*If?*" asked Vera. "I don't remember any *if* in the Scout Law. Is there an *if* in it?"

"No," said Dick, "not in writing, anyway. But you can't expect me to be friendly to people who don't deserve to have friends."

"I don't know any such people," said Vera, "and I don't think you do, either. What did Sid do that makes you think he doesn't deserve your friendship? What did he do that makes you so unkind, so discourteous, and so unfriendly that you shut the door on him when he tries to be friendly?"

270

1. In the first scene of this story you learned that Dick thought he had no friends. In the second scene you learned how Dick and Sid, who once were pals, felt about each other.

   a. Which boy did not understand why they were no longer friends?

   b. Which boy tried to be friendly again?

2. Dick seemed to think that the other boys did not deserve his friendship. He said they could not be counted on.

   a. A Scout is expected to be kind. Dick said of his fellow Scouts, "Not a one of those kids really deserves to be a Scout." Was that a kind thing to say?

   b. A Scout is expected to be friendly. Dick pretended that he did not hear Sid call to him. If Dick had been friendly, would he have pretended not to hear?

   c. A Scout is expected to be courteous. When Dick saw Sid coming, he went inside his house and shut the door. Was that a courteous thing to do?

   d. Dick was careful to shut the door quietly instead of slamming it. Slamming the door would have been a rude thing to do. But can even the quiet closing of a door be unkind, unfriendly, and discourteous?

271

e. A Scout is expected to be trustworthy. A trustworthy person acts the same when he is alone as when he is being watched. Once he was inside his house, Dick put his ear to the door and listened to what Sid and Vera said. If Dick had been as trustworthy as he expected others to be, would he have put his ear to the door?

3. Dick said he could not count on Sid.

    a. Have you been told why not?

    b. Did Sid do anything that leads you to think that he could not be counted on in any way?

    c. It was Sid, not Dick, who called out to the other boy, "Hey, wait a minute!" It was Sid, not Dick, who wished the other boy lots of luck. It was Sid, not Dick, who said, "If he ever needs a friend, he can count on me." Was it Sid, or was it Dick, who could be counted on to live up to the Scout Law as far as kindness, courtesy, and friendliness are concerned?

4. After Dick went inside the house, Vera said to Sid, "Dick must have been thinking so hard about something that he didn't hear you call to him."

    a. You know that Dick only pretended not to hear. Did Vera probably know that, too?

    b. Vera had a choice of being kindly tactful or of being unkindly frank. Which choice did she make?

    c. Vera had a choice of helping her brother by covering up his discourtesy or of hurting him by admitting it. Which choice did she make?

d. In the first scene Vera said that people had told her how much they liked her and how much they would miss her when she moved away. Do your answers to questions 4b and 4c seem to show that Vera was the kind of girl who would be liked that much?

Dick stared at the floor, saying nothing.

"Tell me," Vera insisted. "Tell me why you are unfriendly to Sid."

"Sid doesn't keep his word," said Dick.

"What doesn't he keep his word about?" asked Vera.

"Well," said Dick, "two or three weeks ago I asked Sid to come over and play with me one afternoon. He said he would, but he didn't come. Instead, he called up and said he had to stay home because his cousin had come to see him."

"That sounds like a good reason for not coming to see you," said Vera.

"You're forgetting something," said Dick. "Sid was breaking his word. First he said he would come over here. Then he called up with that excuse about his cousin and tried to back out of what he said he would do."

"Did Sid ask you to go over there and play with him and his cousin?" asked Vera.

"Yes," said Dick. "But I wouldn't go."

"Why not?" asked Vera. Then she added, "Never mind. Don't answer. I know the answer. You wouldn't go to Sid's house because he had agreed to come to yours. You were going to do exactly what you had agreed to do, even if you lost a friend, weren't you?"

"Why not?" asked Dick. "What's wrong with doing exactly what you've agreed to do?"

"Not a thing," said Vera. "Everybody respects a person who does exactly what he has agreed to do. Most people also respect a person who is kind enough and courteous enough and friendly enough to excuse someone who can't do exactly what he has agreed to do."

"You're taking Sid's side, Vera," said Dick.

"No, Dick," said Vera. "I'm on your side because I know that you want to be on the right side. I'm just trying to help you see what is the right side. Look across the street, Dick, at those two pups."

Dick looked. Sid's pups were growling and snapping at each other. Then they backed off, facing each other and barking. When one jumped at the other, they rolled over and over, each feeling with his teeth for the other's throat.

"What are the pups doing, Dick?" asked Vera. "Are they playing or fighting?"

"They're playing," said Dick. "If either one of them got that rough in a real fight, I think the other one would run away."

"Have you seen them try to play that way with the old black dog down the street?" asked Vera.

"Yes, I have," said Dick, "but the old dog won't play with them. He's as unfriendly with the pups as he is with us."

"I remember something that happened here a few weeks ago," said Vera. "You and Sid were wrestling on the lawn and yelling at each other. You made so much noise that Mother thought you

were having a real fight. She called to you and told you to stop. Do you remember that?"

Dick laughed. "Yes," he said. "I remember that. Sid and I stopped pounding each other and started to laugh."

"What were you laughing at?" asked Vera.

"We thought it was funny that Mother would think we were really fighting," said Dick. "She should have known better than that."

"You and Sid were like the two pups then," said Vera. "Now Sid is still like a pup, but you —"

"I know," said Dick. "I've been as unfriendly as that old black dog."

"You and Sid have been friends a long time," said Vera. "Tomorrow you have to move away. Should you and Sid remember each other as you will those two playful pups? Or do you want Sid to remember you as you will that old black dog?"

Dick shook his head. "I haven't been very smart," he said. "If I knew how to make up with Sid, I would. Should I go over and tell him I forgive him?"

"I don't think he has done anything that needs to be forgiven," said Vera.

"Then should I ask him to forgive me?" asked Dick.

"Maybe it would be better for you to take a hint from the pups," said Vera. "Every once in a while, one of them bites too hard. Then the other one goes away by himself for a while. Later, when either one of them wants to play, he just starts playing. The other one always joins in."

"I know just what you mean," said Dick. "Watch this old dog turn into a pup again, right now. Follow me out to the porch again and see what happens."

Dick hurried out to his porch and looked across the street. Sid was sitting on his front steps, with his elbows on his knees and his chin in his hands. Dick let his front door slam shut, and Sid looked up.

"Hey, Sid!" called Dick. "I can beat you to the corner!"

Sid jumped to his feet. "You just think you can!" he shouted.

"Let's go!" yelled Dick, and both boys were off, shouting names at each other as they ran.

Vera watched them go. Sid, she noticed, almost fell over the two pups, which had happily joined the race. And Dick had to turn out to keep from running into the old black dog, which acted as if it had the whole sidewalk to itself.

The corner was too far away for Vera to tell which boy reached it first. No matter who won, there would be an argument about it. And the argument would probably end in a tussle.

"Good!" Vera said to herself. "Only friends tussle."

Down the street, toward Vera, came the old black dog. "Come here, boy," she called. "Let me give you one friendly pat, just to say good-by." The old dog walked on past without turning its head.

"Good-by, black dog," said Vera. "I'm glad my brother is no longer like you. Dick had sense enough to change. I'm sorry for you because you don't have that much sense."

The old black dog kept on walking. He kept on looking straight ahead.

thinking about what you have read

1. Dick's reason for being unfriendly to Sid was that Sid had not kept his word.

    a. Had Sid offered a good reason for not keeping his word?

    b. Was it a reason that Dick should have accepted?

    c. If either boy had a right to feel offended, which one was it?

2. Dick proved himself to be unreasonable, unfriendly, unkind, and discourteous. Yet Sid still wanted to be friendly with him, and Vera still wanted to help him.

280

a. Did Sid and Vera prove that they could like a person even if they did not like some of the things he did?

b. Did they prove that friendship does not have to be deserved?

3. The old black dog and the two pups are important in this story.

a. When one of the pups was wiggling, wagging its tail, and licking someone's hand, was it acting like Dick or like Sid?

b. At times the pups chased each other, knocked each other down, and barked and snapped at each other. When were Dick and Sid like the pups — before they quarreled or after?

c. When the old black dog paid no attention to anyone who tried to be friendly with it, was it like Dick, like Sid, or like Vera?

4. In the last scene Dick said, "Watch this old dog turn into a pup again, right now."

a. Did he mean the old black dog outside, or did he mean himself?

b. Did he mean, "I'm no longer going to be as unfriendly as the old dog, but I'm going to be as friendly as the pups"?

5. Vera knew that Dick would soon be in a new neighborhood in Colton.

a. There in Colton, perhaps across the street or in the house next door, Dick would probably find a boy like Sid. Now that Dick was no longer acting like the old black dog, would he be likely to make friends with that boy?

b. There in Colton, Dick would surely find a troop of Scouts he could join. Now that Dick was no longer acting like the old black dog, would he be likely to make friends with those Scouts?

c. Wherever he went, in Colton or anywhere else, Dick would take with him a lesson he had learned from the pups and the old black dog. Was it a lesson in how to be trustworthy or in how to be friendly?